It's another Quality Book from CGP

This book is for anyone doing OCR GCSE Science — Staged Assessment.

It contains lots of tricky questions designed
to make you sweat — because that's the only
way you'll get any better.

It's also got some daft bits in to try and make
the whole experience at least vaguely
entertaining for you.

What CGP is all about

Our sole aim here at CGP is to produce the highest quality
books — carefully written, immaculately presented, and dangerously
close to being funny.

Then we work our socks off to get them out to you
— at the cheapest possible prices.

Contents
Year 11 Workbook

Contents
Year 11 Workbook

Contributors:
Matthew Ball
Chris Bates
Charley Darbishire
Gemma Hallam
Simon Little
Toby Langley
Tim Major
Tessa Moulton
Pratheeban Nambyiah
Alison Palin
Andy Park
Sam Patterson
Philip Robson
Julie Schofield
Claire Thompson
Suzanne Worthington

Based on original questions by:
Jane Cartwright
Chris Christofi
Bill Doling
Paddy Gannon
Alex Kizildas
Nigel Saunders

With thanks to David Worthington and Eileen Worthington for the proofreading

Published by Coordination Group Publications Ltd
ISBN 1 84146 958 0
Groovy Website: www.cgpbooks.co.uk

Printed by Elanders Hindson, Newcastle upon Tyne.
Clipart sources: CorelDRAW and VECTOR.

Variation

You and your mates don't look the same. Ever wondered why that is... Nope.
Well anyway, your characteristics are "both inherited and due to environmental factors".

Q1   Identical twins have the same genes, so they are
genetically identical. The table shows four people,
identified by the letters a, b, c and d.

	Person			
Characteristic	a	b	c	d
Have a sun tan	✔	✔		
They are male	✔	✔	✔	
They are female				✔
Can tongue roll	✔		✔	
Normal hair colour is brown	✔	✔	✔	✔
Have bleached white hair			✔	✔
Have brown eyes	✔	✔	✔	

a)   **i)**   **Use** the information in the table to identify
which two people are identical twins.

ii)   **Explain** your answer.

b)   Give **one characteristic** which shows:
i)   Continuous variation.
ii)   Discontinuous variation.

*Note — tongue rolling has
a direct genetic cause.*

Q2   People belong to one of these four blood groups: A, B, AB and O.

Copy and complete the paragraph below using some of the words in the box.

discontinuous   environmental   inherited   range
Our blood group is _____ and is not altered by _____ conditions. Blood group shows _____ variation.

Q3   Try these questions about genes and different characteristics.

a)   **Where** are chromosomes found in the body?
b)   **How many pairs** of human chromosomes are there?
c)   Which of the characteristics in the box below are **totally inherited**?
That is, which are determined **only** by the alleles you inherit from your
parents?

body weight, hair colour, academic ability, blood group, health, inherited diseases, eye colour, skin colour, sporting ability

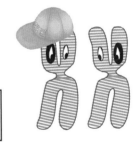

d)   The other characteristics in the list may be affected by something else.
What else might they be affected by?

Q4   The jumbled list on the right shows
different human characteristics.

a)   Which of these characteristics show:
i)   **continuous** variation?
ii)   **discontinuous** variation?

b)   Which of the features are:
i)   affected by the **environment**?
ii)   **not** affected by the environment?

Eye Colour

Weight

Fitness (measured by resting pulse)

Hair Colour

Intelligence

Height

c)   Give the characteristic **least** affected by inheritance.
d)   Choose any one feature and explain **how** it is affected by the environment.

Variation

A day with variety is like a warm Summer day — bright and exciting...

Q5   Pick the correct word from each highlighted pair to complete the sentences below.

a)   Mitosis is a process used during growth and **asexual** / **sexual** reproduction.

b)   When mitosis is complete, **two** / **three** daughter cells are produced.

c)   Each daughter cell produced by mitosis has **the same** / **a different** number of chromosomes as the parent.

d)   Meiosis is a **multiplication** / **reduction** process — this means that the number of chromosomes in the original cell is **doubled** / **halved**.

e)   **Mitosis** / **meiosis** is used in the production of male and female **gametes** / **gammon**.

f)   **Mitosis** / **meiosis** involves some jumbling of genetic material, so producing variation.

Q6   Genes, chromosomes and DNA are important things you need to know about.

a)   **Draw** simple diagrams of the items listed in the box below.

cell,   nucleus,   chromosome,   gene,   DNA

b)   **Humans show lots of variation** in eye colour, hair colour, etc.
Explain how **genes** give rise to this variation.

c)   **Copy and complete** the following sentences using each word from the box below once.

new   divide   growth   multiply   divide   identical   replicating   replace
Body cells _____ to produce _____ cells that are _____ to the original cell. The new cells continue to _____ and _____ by _____ themselves. The cells produced are used for _____ and also to _____ old cells.

Q7   Are the following statements **true** or **false**? If a statement is false, say what the word in bold would need to be to make the sentence true.

a)   The **DNA** contains the chromosomes that carry the genes.

b)   Different species have different numbers of **chromosomes**.

c)   Humans have 23 pairs of **cells** (ie. 46 altogether).

d)   This means that 23 is the **diploid** number.

e)   Chromosomes are made up of a double helix of **DNA**.

f)   A gene is a portion of DNA that acts as a code for the production of a particular **protein**.

g)   When cells **divide** the DNA has to be copied accurately.

Q8   This is a typical animal cell.

a)   What **part** of the cell are chromosomes found in?
b)   How do the chromosomes carry genetic information?
c)   If this was a human cell, **how many** chromosomes would be inside it?
d)   What is the **chemical** that chromosomes are made of?

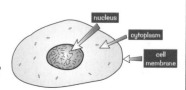

Mutations

Q1   Complete the blanks by using the following words:

> antibiotics beneficial carcinogens divide genetic sex harmful ionising
> mitosis mutagens mutations naturally neutral chromosome nucleus replication

A mutation is a change in a gene or a _____ (change in the genetic code). Different genes can result from such a change. Mutations can occur _____ when DNA is incorrectly copied during _____. Gene mutations may start in a single _____ of one cell. As the cells _____ to produce more cells, the number of cells carrying the new form increases. The chance of _____ occurring can be increased by exposure to _____ radiation, X-rays, ultra-violet light and also certain chemicals (mutations can also occur spontaneously). The greater the dose, the greater the chance of mutations occurring. Chemicals that cause mutations are called _____ and include substances found in cigarette smoke. Such substances are called _____ because they can increase the chance of people having cancer. Most mutations are _____. If mutations occur in _____ cells, the children may develop abnormally. This can result in early death. Mutations that occur in body cells can cause uncontrollable cell division (_____), resulting in cancer. Some mutations are _____ in their effects, causing no apparent harm or benefit to the individual. On rare occasions, a mutation can be _____, increasing an organism's chances of survival. Bacteria mutating has definitely benefited them by giving them resistance to the _____ we use against them. Mutation is the source of _____ variation. Changing by acquiring new forms of old genes is how living things have evolved by natural selection.

Q2   In our everyday lives we are subject to different mutation-causing influences.

a)   **Why** do doctors recommend that you use suncream when sunbathing?
b)   **What precautions** must a radiographer take when taking an X-ray of you and why?
c)   **Why** is carbon tetrachloride no longer used as a cleaning agent by dry cleaners?

Earlier this century radioactive paints were used when making watches and clocks to make the numbers glow in the dark.

d)   **Why** do you think many workers who made these clocks later developed throat and mouth cancer?

Q3   Most body cells in an organism have the same number of chromosomes. Copy this table about different animals' chromosomes. Then fill in the missing information.

Organism	Number of chromosomes in a body cell	Number of pairs of chromosomes	Number of chromosomes in each gamete
Fruit Fly	8		
Kangaroo	12		
Rye Plant	20		
Chicken	36		
Mouse	40		
Humans	46		
Crayfish	200		

<u>Ordinary Cell Division : Mitosis</u>

Q1 Copy the table below. Then put these sentences in the correct columns, depending on whether they describe sexual or asexual reproduction.

| Male and female gametes join | No joining of sex cells needed |

| Offspring are not genetically identical to parents | Only one parent is needed |

| Offspring are clones of parent | Two parents are needed |

Asexual Reproduction	Sexual Reproduction

Q2 Describe what's happening at each of the numbered stages in the diagrams below.

Diagram **A** –
the stages involved
in cell reproduction
by **mitosis**.

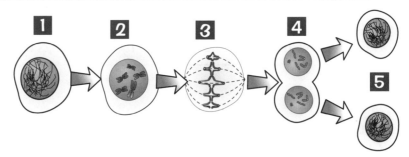

Diagram **B** –
the stages involved
in cell reproduction
by **meiosis**.

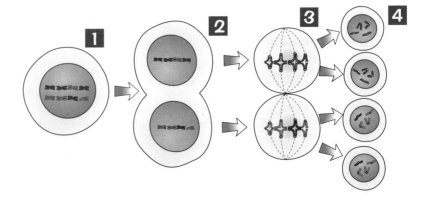

<u>Mitosis and meiosis — sounds like a dodgy comedy duo...</u>

Clever stuff this cell reproduction — I'm just glad it takes care of itself. You need to know all of the stuff on this page, so make sure you keep going until the answers come to mind easily...

Fertilisation: The Meeting of Gametes

Life would be pretty dull if everyone was the same.
I mean everyone would have the same name — Dan, obviously.

Q1 The diagram shows the progress from sex cells to a baby.

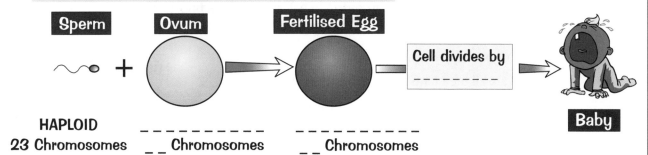

Sperm + **Ovum** → **Fertilised Egg** → **Cell divides by** _ _ _ _ _ _ _ _ → **Baby**

HAPLOID
23 Chromosomes _
_ _ Chromosomes _ _ Chromosomes

a) **Complete** the five spaces in the diagram above.

b) Name the **reproductive** organs that produce:

   i)   sperm cells.

   ii)   ova.

c) What word also means **sperm** or **egg** cells?

d) What is another name for a **fertilised egg**?

e) What do we call the **process** where sperm and egg cells join together?

f) **Where** does fertilisation take place in the body of the human female?

Q2 Use the following words to fill in the blanks in the passage below.

| children | chromosome | diploid | egg | fertilisation | gametes |
| meiosis | ova | ovaries | sperm | testes | variation |

Sexual reproduction involves the production of _____, followed by
_____. Random combination of chromosomes in _____ creates
genetic _____ amongst the sperm and _____ cells produced.
The random fusion of gametes gives rise to variation in the _____. The
male gametes are the _____ cells and the female gametes are the egg
cells (also called _____). Male gametes are produced in the
_____ and female gametes are produced in the _____.
The gametes contain one _____ from each homologous pair.
When fertilisation occurs, these chromosomes come together to produce the
correct _____ number, which in humans is 46.

Variety is the spice of life, or is it green chillies...

Genetic variation is dead important stuff — I mean without it we'd all be in real trouble. Fertilisation is one of the key ways of introducing variety into organisms, so make sure you can answer all of these questions really easily. If you can't do it now, you definitely won't be able to do it in the exam...

Cloned Plants

We humans love plants just the way they are — we like them so much that we go to loads of effort to clone them. What do we end up with — exactly what we started with. Great.

Q1 The UK exports date-palms to Iran and oil-palms to Malaysia. The reason we can do this is because Britain has advanced technology for tissue culturing. The diagram shows how tissue culturing works.

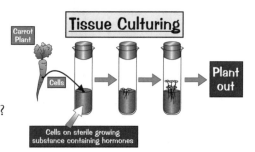

a) What type of **reproduction** is this?

b) i) Why are all the plants produced **identical**?

  ii) What name is given to **identical** offspring?

c) i) What are the **advantages** of using tissue cultures?

  ii) What are the **disadvantages** of using tissue cultures?

d) What **other** technique produces identical plants?

Q2 Parts of plants that are grown into new plants are called cuttings.

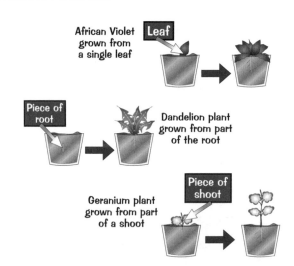

a) **What type** of reproduction is shown here?

b) What **conditions** are needed for the cuttings to develop?

c) **How** do the plants on the right of the diagram **compare genetically** with the plants that the cuttings were taken from?

d) **How** do seeds from these plants **compare genetically** with the parent plants?

e) i) Give two **advantages** of taking cuttings.

  ii) Give two **disadvantages** of taking cuttings.

Q3 Choose the correct word from inside the brackets to complete the sentences.

a) Plants produced from cuttings grow into new plants by (**meiotic** / **mitotic**) cell division.

b) Tissue cultures are a useful way of producing large numbers of (**different** / **identical**) plants with the desired characteristics from a small number of cells.

c) Genetically identical plants are produced by (**asexual** / **sexual**) reproduction.

d) Growing plants from tissue cultures (**decreases** / **increases**) the gene pool.

e) Cloning techniques are also used in producing identical animals by splitting embryo cells (**after** / **before**) they specialise.

f) Tissue cultures need a (**large** / **small**) number of tissue pieces, (**aseptic** / **diseased**) conditions, and growth medium.

Cloned Plants

Q4 Use each of the following words once to fill in the blanks in this passage:

asexual	cells	cuttings	embryo	genetically	host
	identical	mitosis	naturally	splitting	tissue

Clones are _____ identical organisms. Clones of plants are produced during _____ reproduction when _____ takes place. Examples include reproduction by bulbs (like daffodils), stem tubers (potatoes) and runners (strawberries or spider plants), as well as _____. Using _____ culture also results in genetically _____ offspring. This technique involves growing new plants from small groups of _____ from part of a plant. Cloning techniques are also used in producing identical cells in agriculture. This is done by _____ embryo cells (before they become specialised) from a developing animal _____ and then transplanting the identical embryos into a _____ mother. Clones are also produced _____ as in the case of identical twins.

Q5 The diagram shows how animal clones, like cattle, are produced in agriculture. (This is not how Dolly the sheep was made, by the way).

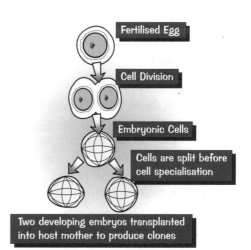

Fertilised Egg

Cell Division

Embryonic Cells

Cells are split before cell specialisation

Two developing embryos transplanted into host mother to produce clones

a) By what **process** does the fertilised egg divide?

b) Why are the two offspring produced called **clones**?

c) **i)** What are the **advantages** of using this technique?

ii) What are the **disadvantages** of using this technique?

Q6 Are these sentences **true or false**? Correct the sentences which are **false**.

a) Plants produce exact copies of themselves by **sexual** reproduction.

b) Plant reproduction can take place **without** the need for another plant.

c) Asexual reproduction produces **more** variation than sexual reproduction.

d) Sexual reproduction requires only **one** parent.

e) **Genetic information** from both parents is **combined** in sexual reproduction.

Top-tips: Plants — don't say much, don't listen to what you say, don't even take exams. They do some cool stuff though. Imagine if you could cut off your finger and it would grow into a whole new person. Then there'd be two yous. So you'd only have to do half the work, half the revision. Imagine...

Module BD4 — Variation, Inheritance and Evolution

Monohybrid Crosses: Terminology

This section's all about sex — well almost, there's a bit on chromosomes as well...

Q1   Answer these questions on chromosomes and DNA.

a)   What are chromosomes made of?

b)   Chromosomes are made of four separate arms — what name is given to these?

c)   The centromere connects the chromatids together.
Where is this found?

d)   What is a gene?

Different versions of the same gene are called alleles.

e)   Alleles which determine the characteristic of an individual
are given a special name. What is it?

f)   What does it mean if a person is homozygous?

g)   If the person has different alleles then they are known as heterozygous.
In this case what characteristic will the person have.

Q2   Answer these questions:

a)   Copy and complete the diagram which shows how sex is inherited.

b)   Work out from the diagram the **ratio** of boys to girls.

c)   A couple have one child, Janet. The couple are convinced that their next child will be a boy because they already have a daughter. Is this true?
Explain your answer.

d)   Genotypes of offspring can also be worked out with a checkerboard-type diagram (sometimes called a Punnett Square).
Complete the diagram to the right.

Parents' Phenotype :	————	————
Parents' Genotype :	X X	X _
Gametes' Genotype :	X X	X _
Childrens' Genotype :	_ _ X Y	X X _ _
Childrens' Phenotype :	—— ——	—— ——

Q3   In the old days, kings were known to behead their wives for not giving them sons.

a)   What sex chromosomes do **sperm** cells have?

b)   What sex chromosomes do **egg** cells have?

c)   i)   Is it the man's or woman's gametes that determine the **sex** of the child?
ii)   **Explain** your answer.

Chop off her head!!

Genotype — the new Jaguar car...

Alleles, genotypes, phenotypes — they can sound quite scary when you don't know what they are, so learn how to answer these questions and you won't be worrying in the exam. It's helpful to copy out the diagrams yourself a few times until you've got the hang of them, so get going...

Module BD4 — Variation, Inheritance and Evolution

Monohybrid Crosses: Terminology

More on chromosomes and breeding I'm afraid — still at least there's some
diagrams to brighten up the section...

Q4 The diagram shows a cross between a black male mouse and a brown female mouse.

a) What does **homozygous** mean?

b) Why are some genes **represented** by "B" and others by "b"?

c) Explain **why B** and b are alleles.

d) The F1 are all heterozygous black.

    i) What does **F1** stand for?

    ii) What does **heterozygous** mean?

e) i) Which allele is **dominant**?

    ii) **Explain** what dominant means.

f) i) What does **genotype** mean?

    ii) What does **phenotype** mean?

Parents' Phenotype :	Homozygous Black Male	Homozygous Brown Female
Parents' Genotype :	BB	bb
Gametes' Genotype :	B B	b b
Offsprings' Genotype :	Bb Bb	Bb Bb
Offsprings' Phenotype :	All Heterozygous Black	

g) Two individuals from the F1, a male and a female, are taken and mated.

    i) Use a **checkerboard-type** diagram to show the cross.

    ii) What are the possible **phenotypes** and **genotypes** of the offspring?

    iii) What is the **ratio** of the phenotypes of the offspring?

    iv) What do we call this generation?

Q5 A brown eyed man married a blue eyed woman. The allele for brown eyes is
dominant and that for blue eyes is recessive. (The father is heterozygous for the gene).

a) What **letters** would you use for the brown and blue alleles?

b) **Complete** the cross by filling in the spaces.

c) Which individuals are **homozygous**?

d) How is it **possible** for two brown eyed individuals to have a blue eyed baby?

Parents' Phenotype :	Blue eyed mother	Brown eyed father
Parents' Genotype :	————	————
Gametes' Genotype :	—— ——	—— ——
Offsprings' Genotype :	—— ——	—— ——
Offsprings' Phenotype :	—— ——	—— ——

Q6 Fill in the blanks using each of these words once.

alleles   F1   F2   genotype   height
heterozygous   homozygous   monohybrid   phenotype   recessive

In _____ crosses, we only cross for one characteristic, such as _____ in pea plants
or colour in mice. Each gene has two different forms — these are called _____.
The allele whose characteristic is masked in the presence of a dominant gene is _____.
If an individual has two alleles the same for a particular gene, we say they are _____
but if they have different alleles, they are _____. The word _____ refers to the
appearance or the physical characteristic that results, whereas _____ refers to the
alleles present. In genetic crosses, we talk about different generations. The _____
represents the children and the _____ the grandchildren.

Genetic Diseases

Inheritance is why you don't look like your chums — but you do look like your mam and dad.

Q1 Inherited diseases are caused by faulty genes, most of
which are recessive. Use these words to fill in the blanks.

allele	both	carriers	genetic
	membranes	recessive	

Cystic fibrosis is a _____ disease. One in twenty people in this country carry the
recessive allele. Sufferers must have two _____ alleles. Cystic fibrosis is a disorder
of cell _____. In the lungs, the membranes produce thick sticky mucus which makes
breathing more difficult and causes more infections to the lungs. Infections are treated with
antibiotics. The mucus can be removed by regular physiotherapy and massage. Excess
mucus is also produced in the pancreas, causing digestive problems. Sufferers have a
shortened life. Since the disease is caused by a recessive _____, it must be inherited
from _____ parents. Parents who have the recessive allele are _____ of
the disorder. Carriers have no ill-effects themselves.

Q2 The diagram below shows a cross between two people who are unaffected by cystic fibrosis.

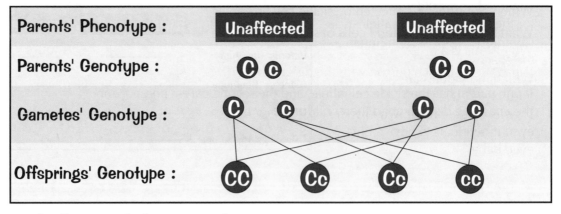

a) From the **diagram**, which genotypes show:
  i) carriers?
  ii) sufferers?
  iii) homozygous?
  iv) heterozygous?

b) What do we mean by **carriers**?

Q3 Complete the sentences by choosing the right word or words from inside the brackets.
  a) Cystic fibrosis is an (**infectious / inherited**) disease.
  b) Cystic fibrosis is caused by a (**dominant / recessive**) allele.
  c) Children can inherit the cystic fibrosis disease when
     (**both / one**) of their parents have the recessive allele.

Genetic Diseases

Q4   The diagram shows a family who have been tested for the cystic fibrosis allele.

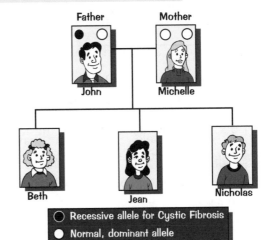

a)   Using appropriate letters, give the **genotypes** of the mother and father.

b)   Will any of the children be **sufferers**?

c)   i) Can you say **which children** will carry a recessive allele?

   ii) **Explain** your answer.

d)   What is the **chance** of Beth being a carrier?

e)   What **proportion** of John and Michelle's children are likely to be **neither carriers nor sufferers**?

f)   i) From the **diagram**, can we tell whether both of the father's parents were **carriers**?

   ii) **Explain** your answer.

Q5   Sickle cell anaemia is an inherited disease. Answer these questions about it.

a)   There are four main components of blood.
      Which component is affected by sickle cell anaemia?

b)   What happens to the blood cells of someone with the disease?
      Why is this is a **problem**?

c)   What **alleles** must a person with the disease have?

d)   If one parent has the sickle cell allele, and the second parent doesn't, can they pass the disease on to their children?

Q6   Map A shows the distribution of the sickle cell allele in Africa.
          Map B shows the distribution of malaria in the same geographical region.

a)   **Why** are the distributions so similar?

b)   Sickle cell anaemia is a **killer** disease.

   i) Give an **advantage** for people who are **carriers** of the disease?

   ii) What is a **disadvantage** for people who are **carriers** of the disease?

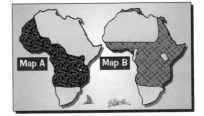

Q7   Genetic engineering has advantages and disadvantages.

a)   What is the main advantage and the main disadvantage of genetic engineering?

b)   Give one ethical issue relating to genetic engineering.

Module BD4 — Variation, Inheritance and Evolution

Selective Breeding / Genetic Engineering

Manky moggies don't win cat shows — breeders look for the
best characteristics to produce the purrfect champion...

Q1   Answer these **true or false** questions on artificial selection.

a)   New breeds and varieties of animals or crops can be produced by artificial selection.

b)   Individuals without any desired characteristics are identified and used for breeding.

c)   Selective breeding isolates the genes of the animals with the useful characteristics.

d)   Because of artificial selection, Friesian cows now produce lower milk yields.

e)   Selective breeding is used to breed/create roses of different shapes and colours.

f)   One disadvantage of selective breeding is that the number of alleles
in a population is reduced.

g)   Because the gene pool is reduced, few harmful recessive characteristics can
exist within the population.

h)   Selective breeding of animals or crops is always beneficial.

Q2   People have produced new breeds of dog to achieve either a particular look or temperament (in
the dog). Some of the features we have bred in dogs, though, are not advantageous to the dog.

Shar-pei   Basset hound   Bedlington   Bulldog

a)   **All dogs** have been bred from **wolf** ancestors. Give **two features** of
wolves that are no longer found in some modern breeds of dogs.

b)   Why are mongrels (random crossbreeds) often **healthier** than pedigree dogs?

Bulldogs have narrow hips. Often these dogs can only give birth if they are assisted by people.

c)   What would **happen** to this breed of dog if people **stopped assisting them** to give birth?

Q3   Choose the correct word from inside the brackets to complete each of the sentences below.

a)   The process of breeding animals for the best characteristics is called (**artificial** / **natural**) selection.

b)   Selective breeding (**increases** / **decreases**) the number of alleles in a population.

c)   Farmers often selectively breed to (**decrease** / **increase**) yields of food produced.

d)   Selective breeding involves (**asexual** / **sexual**) reproduction.

e)   Breeding characteristics like floppy ears into dogs is (**advantageous** / **disadvantageous**) to the dog.

Fossils and Evolution

This section is about how plants and animals change and adapt over millions of years.
You could try looking for fossils in your garden.

Q1 Use each of the following words once to fill in the blanks:

adaptations	characteristics	changed	Darwin
environment	food	evolution	inherit
fittest	nature	organisms	survival	natural

Evolution is about how living things have _____ over millions of years.
Lamarck and _____ had different ideas about how this happened.
Lamarck believed that new structures appeared when there was a need for them
and those that are not used degenerate.

He also proposed that changes acquired in the lifetime of organisms were then
passed on to the offspring. Darwin on the other hand proposed that organisms
with the best _____ to their _____ survive and have
offspring which _____ those adaptations.

Useful characteristics become more common. Less well adapted organisms die
out. All _____ overproduce offspring, which have to compete,
particularly for _____. Disease and predation cause large
numbers of organisms to die. This is called the struggle for existence. This
struggle leads to the _____ surviving. In other words, those
individuals with the most suitable _____ due to natural variation are the
most likely to survive. So, _____ selects the characteristics that are
going to aid _____. This is called _____ selection.
Other organisms which cannot compete gradually become extinct. These
gradual changes are the mechanism by which _____ occurs.

Q2 Place the sentences below in the right order to explain the evolution of the giraffe.

~ **mutation** resulted in some giraffes having longer necks than others.
~ **all** giraffes had **short** necks.
~ **natural selection** resulted in longer-necked offspring surviving.
~ the giraffe population had individuals whose necks **varied** in length.
~ only **long-necked** giraffes **survived** the competition for food.

Don't be a degenerate — evolve with this knowledge...
Whether you're convinced by Darwin's explanations of evolution or not, you need to know about them.
If you get a question on evolution, then go with his ideas... It's what examiners want you to say.

Natural Selection

Finding fossils is a bit like looking back into the past — you get to see how we got here.

Q1   Which of these statements are true and which are false? Correct the false ones.

a)   Darwin's theory of evolution suggested useful characteristics become more common as they are transferred from parent to offspring.

b)   Organisms that adapt well to their environment tend to become extinct.

c)   Darwin's theory of evolution was difficult to accept by many groups of people due to their religious beliefs.

Q2   Fossils help us to see how animals have evolved. There are different ways that fossils can be formed.

Most fossils form from the hardest parts of animals. **Fill in** the missing words in each of the sentences below then match them up to the stages in the diagram.

a)   When they die, hard parts of animals don't _____ easily. _____ collects around the dead animals and they become buried.

b)   The sediment surrounding the _____ remains also turns to rock, but the fossil stays distinct inside the rock.

c)   Over a long period of time the hard parts _____ and are replaced by _____. A rock-like substance is formed in the same shape as the original hard part, known as a fossil.

d)   Fossils formed in this way usually develop from hard parts of animals such as _____ , _____ and _____ .

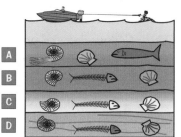

Q3   The diagram shows the earliest occurrence and abundance of fossil vertebrates.

a)   What were the **first vertebrates** to evolve?

b)   Which were the **last vertebrates** to evolve?

c)   How do fossils help us to **understand** evolution?

d)   Although the diagram shows evolution as being continuous, there are missing links in the fossil record of many animals. How can we **explain** these missing links?

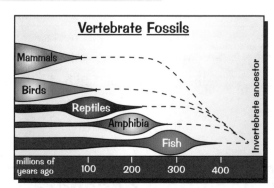

the width of each bar shows the amount of fossils of that age

Photosynthesis

Photosynthesis is just the process by which plants make their food.
Make sure you know all the factors affecting this process — it's an examiner's favourite.

Q1   Photosynthesis mainly takes place in the leaves.
The diagram shows what the leaves need to make **food**.

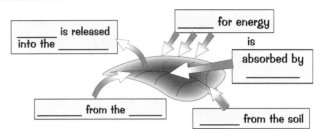

a)   **Complete** the labels on the diagram.

b)   Name the **process** involved in making food.

c)   What is the name of the **food produced**?

Q2   **Complete** the following equation for photosynthesis:

a) with words.   b) as a balanced symbol equation.

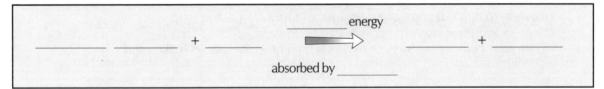

Q3   A variegated geranium has both green and white areas on its leaves.

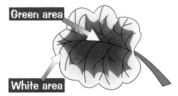
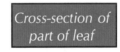

a)   If the diagram were not shaded, how could you tell which cells were the green cells?

b)   What **substance** makes these cells green?

Q4   Adam set up a bottle garden. Inside the bottle he grew some plants and placed a butterfly he caught in his garden. He knew the butterfly fed on sugar, so he placed a dish of sugary water inside the bottle. Just before going on a two week holiday to Corfu, Adam caught another butterfly. He placed this butterfly in another bottle, but he did not have time to add the plants. **The diagrams show** what he saw when he returned from holiday.

a)   Why did the butterfly in the second bottle **die**?

b)   Besides its droppings, what does the first butterfly **produce** that will help the plants to grow?

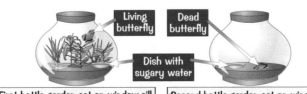

First bottle garden set on window sill   Second bottle garden set on window sill

Top Tips: If you can be sure of any one topic coming up, it's photosynthesis. Life on Earth revolves around it, so make sure that you can answer all of these questions really easily...

Photosynthesis

Q5   Most plants have more pores on the **lower** surface of their leaves.

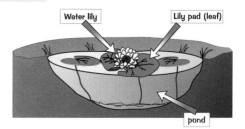

   a)   Water lilies have more pores on their **upper** surface.
            Give a reason for this.

   b)   **Name a gas** that the lily needs for photosynthesis.

   c)   Using the diagram, **describe one other adaptation**
            of the water lily for photosynthesis.

Q6   Leaves are adapted for efficient photosynthesis in many ways.

   a)   Why are leaves **thin** rather than thick? How does this aid photosynthesis?

   b)   Give **three** other features of leaves which make them **efficient** at photosynthesis.

        The cells within the leaf are designed for photosynthesis as well.

   c)   Give **four cellular features** of leaves which help the leaf to make food.

Q7   The graph shows the effect of different conditions on the rate of photosynthesis.

   a)   What is a **limiting factor**?

   b)   **Name a factor** that **limits** the rate of photosynthesis at position **X**.

   c)   **Draw a curve** on the graph to show what would happen
            if the amount of carbon dioxide was **increased** to a much
            higher level (at 30°C).

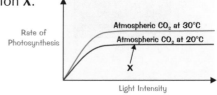

   d)   What time of the year do plants grow **fastest**?

Q8   **Glucose** is a product of **photosynthesis**. Some of it is stored in the roots, stem and leaves of a plant.
         This is then ready for use when photosynthesis isn't happening, like in the winter, or the dark.

   a)   What is this glucose **converted** to before it's **stored**?

   b)   What is it stored as?

Q9   Plant cells use some of the glucose produced during photosynthesis for **respiration**.
         They use the energy released during respiration to build up **smaller** molecules into **larger** ones.

   a)   Name **three** other useful substances, apart from starch, that sugars are converted to.

   b)   What are these **new** substances used for?

Photosynthesis

Q10 The diagram opposite shows a section across a leaf.

a) i) Give two **functions** of a leaf vein.
ii) Name the **cells** carrying out each function.

b) i) What is the fuction of the **pores** in the leaf?
ii) What controls the **size** of the pores?
iii) Why are there more pores on the **underside** of a leaf?

c) i) Give the name for **cell X**.
ii) What is the **main function** of this cell?
iii) Give one way in which this cell is **adapted** for its function.

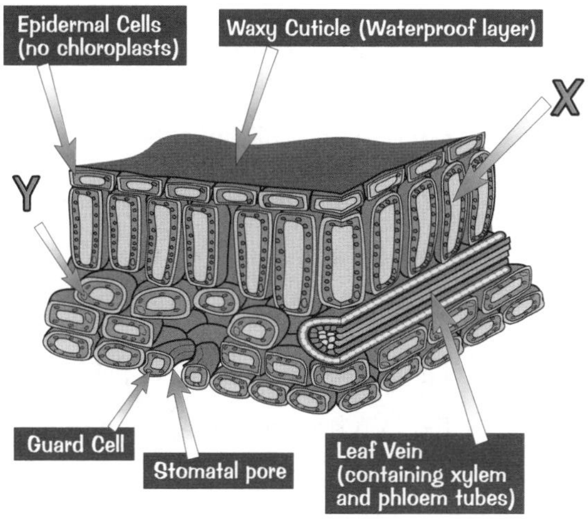

d) i) Give the name for **cell Y**.
ii) These cells are rounded, creating large air spaces between them. Why is this **useful** for the leaf?

e) What is the function of the **waxy cuticle**?

Labels on diagram:
- Epidermal Cells (no chloroplasts)
- Waxy Cuticle (Waterproof layer)
- X
- Y
- Guard Cell
- Stomatal pore
- Leaf Vein (containing xylem and phloem tubes)

Q11 Match the statement with the correct part of a leaf, for example **A) — ii)** or **B) — ii)**.

A) Contains chloroplasts

B) Contains chlorophyll

C) Green substance

D) Contains xylem & phloem cells

i) Palisade cell

ii) Chlorophyll

iii) Chloroplast

iv) Vein

Q12 Complete the blanks with these words:

carbon dioxide   chlorophyll   chloroplasts   guard cells   mesophyll
palisade   stomata   veins   waxy cuticle   xylem

The leaf is the organ where food is made in a plant. Its _____ cells are packed closely together. These cells have many _____ which contain the green substance _____. This substance absorbs light. The spongy _____ is so called because it has many air spaces. _____ _____ diffuses easily through these spaces to get inside the leaf cells. To make sugar, water is also needed. Water is transported to the leaf cells by _____ vessels. The transporting vessels are inside the _____ of the leaves. To prevent water loss, the surface of the leaf is covered by a _____ _____. To allow gases to move in and out of the leaf, there are many _____, mainly on the lower surface. The size of the stomatal pores is controlled by the _____ _____.

Top Tips: Knowing your <u>leaf structure</u> boils down to knowing the various cell types. There are only a few — but you've really got to know their <u>functions</u> and how they carry them out. <u>Practise</u> drawing them — so you can <u>recognise</u> them when they come up in the Exam.

Module B05 — The Working Plant

Diffusion

Q1   By what **process** does **carbon dioxide** enter leaves and cells?

Q2   Give the definition of **osmosis**.

        What can osmosis be considered a special case of?

Q3   Plant cells draw water into themselves by **osmosis**.

    a)   How does the **pressure** inside a cell change when water moves into it?

    b)   Explain how this effect provides **support** for the plant tissues.

    c)   Why does the plant need an **inelastic cell wall**?

    d)   **Explain** what happens to a plant when there is no water in the soil.

Q4   An experiment was set up using the equipment on the right.

    a)   Explain why the distilled water in the beaker **became coloured**.

    b)   Why did the sugar solution **move up** the capillary tube?

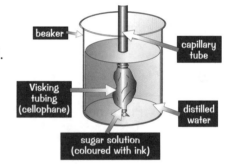

Q5   This is a diagram of a **guard cell** — they are found in leaves.
Guard cells form pores between them called **stomata**.

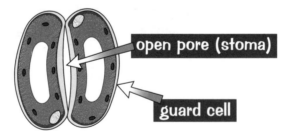

    a)   To **bend and open** the pore (stoma), guard cells must take up water from the surrounding cells.

       i)   What **process** is involved when water enters the guard cells?

       ii)   **Why** does this process happen?

    b)   **Gases** can move through the pore.

       i)   Name **two** gases that can enter and leave plants through the pore.

       ii)   What is the name of the process when **molecules** move in this way?

    c)   Stomatal pores are affected by **light intensity** and the availability of **water**.

       i)   What happens in **bright light** conditions?

       ii)   Do the pores open or close when water is plentiful? **Why** is this?

The Transpiration System

Transpiration is a vital process which helps plants to survive.
More importantly, you need to know it for your exam...

Q1   Flowering plants have separate transport systems for **water** and **nutrients**.

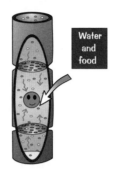
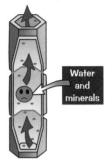

a)   **Name** the type of cells water travels through to reach
the leaves from the stem. Why are these cells **hollow**?

b)   What else is **transported** in these cells?

c)   **Food** is made in the leaves.
What **type** of cells transport this food?
Why are the ends of the cells **perforated**?

d)   What **parts** of the plant is food transported to?

e)   What does the **transported** food consist of?

f)   How are these tubes **arranged** in stems and leaves?

Q2   **Complete the blanks** in the paragraph below with these words.

cuticle   evaporation   greater   guard   leaves   lower   stomata
temperature   thicker   transpiration   xylem   wilt

Plants need to lose water by _____ in order to draw water through the plant
(balance the water loss with water uptake). This cools the plant, provides water for
photosynthesis, supports the plant, and helps minerals to be transported. Water travels
through the _____ from the roots to the _____. The leaves have pores,
called _____, through which most water is lost. The size of the pores is
controlled by _____ cells. Normally, a plant has more pores on the _____
surface of its leaves. Things that affect _____ also affect the rate of water loss
from the leaves. Factors include light, _____, air movements and the amount of
moisture in the air. The drier the air is, the _____ the loss of water from the
leaves. If this loss were to continue, the plant would _____. Leaves are
covered by a waxy _____ to prevent too much water being lost. Plants found in
drier habitats tend to have a _____ waxy layer.

Q3   The graph below shows what effect the size of the stomata has on the **rate of transpiration**.

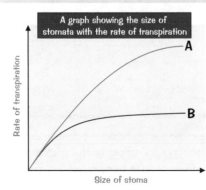

One curve shows what happens in still air and
the other in moving air.

a)   Which curve represents a plant that is
surrounded by **still air**?

b)   How does the difference in air movement
affect the **rate** of transpiration?

c)   Which curve resembles more closely what
happens on a **hot day**? Explain your answer.

The Transpiration System

Q1   A piece of blue cobalt chloride paper was stuck to the upper and lower surfaces of a leaf. Cobalt chloride turns pink as it becomes moist.

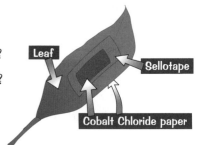

a)   Which **surface** will turn the cobalt chloride pink first? Explain your answer.

b)   What do we call the **process** by which water is lost from the leaf?

c)   From where did the plant obtain the **water** that is lost from the leaf?

d)   Give one condition that **slows down** water loss from leaves.

Q2   The apparatus on the right is called a potometer. As the geranium stem draws water through the cut end of the stem up the capillary tube, the air bubble in the capillary tube moves up.

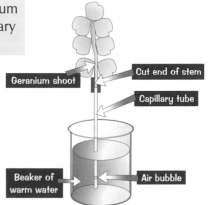

a)   Explain why the amount of water **lost** from the leaves is not the same as the amount of water **taken up** by the stem.

b)   By what process is water lost from the **surface** of the leaves?

c)   What type of **cells** does the water travel through to reach the leaves from the stem?

d)   What else is **transported** in these cells?

Q3   In most plants, the stomata are more open during the day and more closed during the night. In cacti (hot desert plants), the reverse is true.

a)   Give a possible **reason** for this.

b)   Explain exactly **how** the size of the stomata are controlled.

Q4   The table below gives the number of stomata found in five different species of plant. One of these plants is Oat, where the leaves are upright. This means that there is no clear lower and upper leaf surface.

a)   **i) Which letter** represents the oat plant?
        ii) Give one reason for your answer.

b)   Give two **functions** of stomata.

c)   **i)** Name an **atmospheric factor** that affects one of the functions.
        ii) Explain your answer.

Plant	Average number of stomata (per cm²)	
	Lower Surface	Upper Surface
A	2 300	2 500
B	16 100	5 100
C	46 100	0
D	26 300	6 000
E	1 900	5 900

Top Tips: Transpiration isn't the same as evaporation: <u>transpiration</u> is the movement of a whole water column through a plant — it doesn't just happen at a surface. But <u>evaporation</u> draws the water up so they're affected by the same things — make sure you can list them.

Minerals and Fertilisers

Minerals and fertilisers help plants to grow, develop,
take over the world — well the first two at least.

Q1 On the surface of roots there are special cells called **root hair cells**.

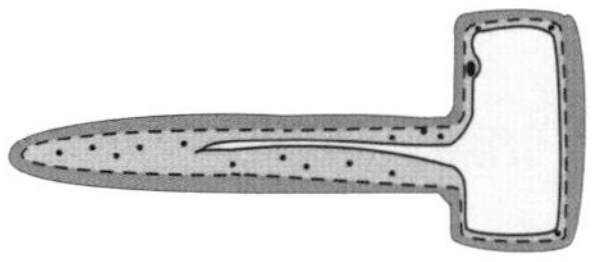

a) How are these cells **adapted** to perform a specific function?
Explain how the adaptation helps them to carry out this function.

b) Name two **features** shown in the diagram that tell us that this is a plant cell.

Q2 Substances are sometimes absorbed against a **concentration gradient**.
Fill in the gaps using the words given. You can use each word more than once.

The concentration of minerals is _____ in the root hair cell of a plant

than in the _____ around it. So normal _____ doesn't explain

how minerals are taken into the root hair cell. The process involved here is

called _____ _____. This allows the plant to absorb minerals

against the _____ _____. This is essential for _____.

_____ _____ requires the use of energy from _____.

> soil   concentration gradient   active transport
> growth   respiration   diffusion   higher

Q3 For healthy growth plants need **mineral ions** which are absorbed
by the roots. Complete the sentences below using some of these words:

> nitrates   photosynthesis
> enzymes   proteins
>   fertiliser   magnesium
> potassium   phosphate
>   respiration

Plants need _____ for the synthesis of _____,
and _____ to produce chlorophyll. Plants can absorb
_____ in solution through their roots. Fertilisers contain
minerals such as nitrates, _____, _____ and
magnesium. These are all used by the plant to grow.

Minerals and fertilisers — really it's all just a load of ...

Minerals and fertilisers are easy enough to learn about, so do yourself a favour and learn about them
— if it comes up in the exam you've got some easy marks in the bag straight away. You also need to
know how the plants get these minerals through their root cells. Make sure you can answer them all.

Respiration

Q1 The table opposite should show the approximate percentages of oxygen, carbon dioxide and nitrogen in a person's inhaled and exhaled breath.

Copy and complete the table placing the muddled percentages provided in their correct places. The percentages are **0.04**, **78**, **4**, **78**, **16** and **21**.

GAS	% in inhaled air	% in exhaled air
oxygen		
carbon dioxide		
nitrogen		

Q2 Answer these questions about both aerobic and anaerobic respiration:

> glucose + _____ → _____ + water (+ energy transferred)

a) **Copy and complete** the word equation for aerobic respiration.
b) The chemical symbol for **glucose** is $C_6H_{12}O_6$.
Write the symbol equation for aerobic respiration.
c) What substances are **needed** for respiration? How does each substance travel to where it is used in the body? Where do these substances come from?
d) What substances are **produced** by respiration? How do these substances leave the body?
e) **What else** is produced by respiration?

Q3 Anaerobic respiration occurs when there is a **shortage of oxygen** in the cells.

Use these words to fill in the spaces (words may be used more than once):

less   *incomplete*   *water*   **carbon dioxide**
   aerobic   *oxidise*   *oxygen debt*   *glucose*

Anaerobic respiration is the _____ breakdown of _____ and produces lactic acid. Because the breakdown of glucose is _____ , much _____ energy is released than during _____ respiration. Anaerobic respiration results in an _____ _____ that has to be repaid in order to _____ lactic acid to _____ _____ and _____ .

Q4 Match up the following phrases to the correct type of **respiration** - aerobic, anaerobic or both:

Uses **glucose** and **oxygen**.
Produces **lactic acid**.
Results in an **oxygen debt**.
Produces **carbon dioxide** and **water**.
Releases **energy**.
Uses **glucose** without oxygen.
Releases the **least** energy

Aerobic Respiration

Anaerobic Respiration

Aerobic <u>and</u> anaerobic respiration

Respiration

Q5 David does a simple experiment to investigate respiration and muscle activity.
He rapidly clenches and unclenches his fist, counting how many times he can do this
before his hand feels like it's going to fall off. His results are shown in the table.

a) Why are David's muscles unable to keep on **contracting**?
What chemical causes the pain he feels?

b) Why can David keep his muscles working much
longer with his hand lowered?

Number of clenches	
hand lowered	hand raised
68	19

Q6 Georgina Henripro has entered a running race. The graph shows the amount
of lactic acid in her blood and her rate of oxygen uptake during the race.
The race takes place between the times marked **A** and **B** on the graph.

a) What type of respiration is most
likely to be occurring when
Georgina is resting before the race?

b) Why does her **rate of oxygen** uptake
increase when she begins to run?

c) Why does Georgina's **rate of oxygen**
uptake reach a maximum during the race?
Why can't she take up any more oxygen
than this?

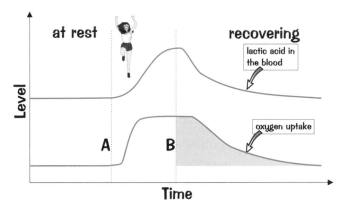

d) Why does the concentration of **lactic acid** in her blood increase during the race?

e) The concentration of lactic acid in Georgina's blood and her rate of oxygen uptake take time to
return to **resting levels** after the race. Explain why.

f) The **shaded area** on the graph is known as the **oxygen debt**. What does this mean?

Q7 Respiration produces carbon dioxide, which is toxic if the levels in the blood are too high.

What happens when the carbon dioxide levels in the blood get too high?

Top Tips: There are definitely a few things within this respiration topic that can get
muddled up. Remember respiration is not breathing in and out, that's
ventilation. These questions will help drill all those definitions into your head.

Module BD6 — Health in the Balance

Maintaining Conditions

To survive, our bodies must keep themselves at just the right temperature, have just the right amount of water and sugar in the bloodstream etc. It's a complicated business — good job the body does it for us. Unfortunately you still need to know how it all works.

Q1   **What** is the ideal internal temperature of the human body?

Q2   This paragraph is about how **body temperature** is controlled. Fill in the gaps using these words. (Words may be used more than once.)

skin   temperature   thermoregulatory
        centre   receptors   impulses

Body temperature is monitored and controlled by the _____ _____ in the brain. This centre has _____ sensitive to the _____ of blood flowing through the brain. Also, temperature _____ in the skin send _____ to the centre giving information about _____ _____ .

Q3   **Complete** this paragraph by choosing the right words.

a)   If the core body temperature is too high, blood vessels supplying the skin capillaries **dilate/ constrict** so that **less/more** blood flows through the capillaries and more heat is lost. If the core temperature is too low, the blood vessels **dilate/constrict** so that **more/less** blood flows through the capillaries and heat is conserved.

b)   Name another way in which the body **cools** itself down.

c)   When the body temperature gets too low, muscles may start to **shiver**.
Explain how this generates heat inside the body.

Q4   Humans need to remove **waste products** from their bodies.

a)   **Carbon dioxide** is produced by respiration. **How** is it removed from the body?

b)   **Urea** is produced in the liver by the breakdown of excess amino acids.
How is urea removed from the body?

Q5   To stay healthy, we need to keep our internal environment fairly **constant**.

a)   Give **three** internal conditions which are controlled by the body.

b)   Name **two** ways in which **water** leaves the body. How does the body get rid of **excess** water?

c)   How does the body lose **ions**? How does it get rid of **excess** ions?

Kidneys and Homeostasis

Q1 The diagram opposite shows part of the system involving the kidneys.

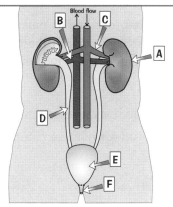

a) **Name** the parts of the system A – F .

b) How does the **blood** travelling through parts **B** and **C** differ?

Q2 Complete the paragraph below about the kidneys using the words provided.

(some of the words can be used more than once, others not at all.)

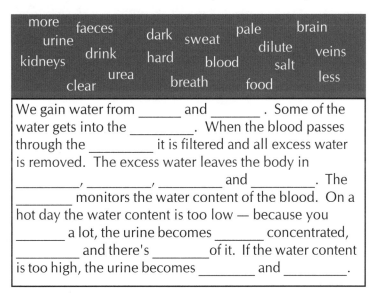

more faeces dark sweat pale brain
urine drink hard blood dilute veins
kidneys salt less
clear urea breath food

We gain water from _____ and _____ . Some of the water gets into the _____. When the blood passes through the _____ it is filtered and all excess water is removed. The excess water leaves the body in _____, _____, _____ and _____. The _____ monitors the water content of the blood. On a hot day the water content is too low — because you _____ a lot, the urine becomes _____ concentrated, _____ and there's _____ of it. If the water content is too high, the urine becomes _____ and _____.

Q3 What does the word homeostasis mean?

Q4 The diagram below is of a vital process in achieving homeostasis.

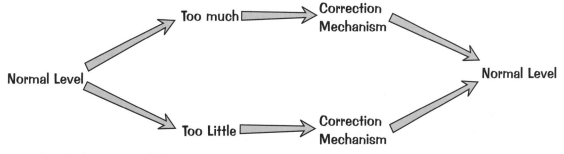

a) **What** is the name of this process?

b) **Explain** the process in the diagram.

c) Give an **example** of the process working in the body.

Fighting Disease

Q1   **Diseases** are more likely to occur if **large** numbers of microorganisms enter the body.
Name **two** factors which result in large numbers of microorganisms entering the body.

Q2   The body has many natural defence systems to **prevent** infection and disease.
List **four** of these natural defences.

Q3   There is one **white cell** to every 600 red cells in the blood. White cells are involved
in protecting the body against infection, and don't just occur in the blood.
Give **three** ways in which white blood cells **protect** us against infection.

Q4   The diagram below shows how **white blood cells** deal with invading microbes.
Label the parts marked **A - D**. .
Your answers to the previous question should help.

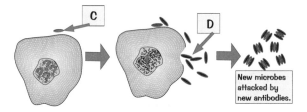

New microbes attacked by new antibodies.

Q5   People are **vaccinated** to help prevent disease.
What are the **two** types of microbe that vaccination protects us against?

Q6   The following paragraph describes how **vaccination** works. Fill in the spaces.
Choose from the words below (you may use words more than once).

| bacterium | immunised | dead | white | antibodies |
| virus | organism | mild | immune | |

When people are vaccinated they are _____ against disease by introducing a
_____ or _____ form of the infecting _____ into their bodies.
The _____ blood cells can respond by producing _____ .
If the infective _____ enters the body, _____ are rapidly produced to
destroy it. This is effective because once they have produced antibodies against a
particular _____ or _____ , white blood cells can quickly produce
them again so that the person is _____ to the disease.

__Drugs__

Even legal drugs such as alcohol and tobacco harm our bodies. People can't make sensible decisions about drugs unless they know the dangers involved. That means being able to answer these questions.

Q1   Fill in the gaps about **addiction**.

a)

> Drugs change the _____ processes in people's bodies so that they may become _____ or _____ to them.

b)   What do people sometimes suffer from when they **stop** taking drugs? Give three examples.

c)   When drug users become addicted they require a larger dose. **Why** is this?

Q2   Apart from its effect on a person's behaviour, alcohol consumption can severely affect the body's ability to function properly.

a)   What **system** in the body is most affected by alcohol in the short term?

b)   What are the **short-term** effects of moderate alcohol consumption?

Q3   Which **two** organs in the body are most prone to damage by long-term excessive alcohol consumption?

Q4   **Smoking** is a serious cause of ill health.

a)   What is the **addictive** substance in tobacco?

b)   Name two **lung diseases**, apart from cancer, caused by smoking tobacco.

c)   Smoking tobacco causes diseases of the **heart** and **blood vessels**.
What do these diseases lead to?

d)   **What** does smoke do to the respiratory system that leads to a 'smoker's cough'?

Q5   Tobacco smoke contains **carbon monoxide**.

a)   How does this carbon monoxide affect the **blood**?

b)   This is especially serious for **pregnant women**. Explain why.

Q6   For every **ten** lung cancer patients, **nine** of them smoke.
Tar in cigarette smoke makes the cells inside the lungs **divide** more than usual.

Suggest how this could lead to **cancer**.

Drugs

Q7   Match up these **drugs** with the **organs** of the body they affect.

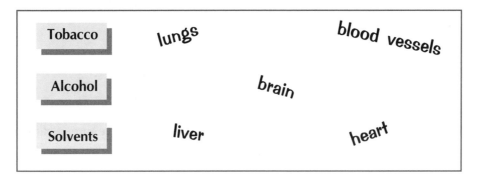

Q8   Remember the **effects** of drinking alcohol and answer these questions:

a)   **Complete** the following sentences on the uses and effects of alcohol:

    (i)   Alcohol is usually used for (**relaxation** / **medicinal purposes**).

    (ii)   It (**slows down** / **speeds up**) the brain and can make you feel less (**inhibited** / **rhythmical**).

    (iii)   However, excessive drinking can lead to damage to the (**liver** / **lungs**) and a drop in (**brain** / **thyroid**) function.

b)   Why is drinking and driving a **lethal** combination?

Q9   Nicotine and caffeine are stimulants and alcohol and solvents are depressants.

a)   What are the effects of stimulants?

b)   What are the effects of depressants?

Q10   Amphetamine is a strong stimulant.

a)   Give **two** long-term effects of using strong stimulants.

b)   **What happens** when the user stops taking them? What **type** of addiction is this?

Q11   Solvents are depressants that have serious effects on the nervous system.

    Explain the effects that solvents have on the nervous system.

Top Tips: Drugs are substances which <u>change</u> the way the body works. Some are helpful (like aspirin and penicillin) but the three on this page have harmful <u>effects</u> — make sure you know them all. In the <u>exam</u>, they'll concentrate on the <u>diseases</u> and all the <u>damage</u> these drugs can do to your body.

Covalent Bonding

Q1   Give the **full electron arrangement** in the following diagrams.

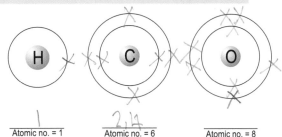

Atomic no. = 1   Atomic no. = 6   Atomic no. = 8

Q2   What is a **molecule?**

Q3   Give **another** name for the joining of two atoms together.

Q4   A covalent bond involves two non-metal atoms sharing what?

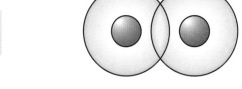

Q5   **Copy** the circles opposite. **Draw** two crosses on them to show the electrons in a single covalent bond:

Q6   Why do atoms **share** electrons?

Q7   **Draw out** the dot and cross diagrams of the following molecules — showing the outer shells only (use the Periodic Table on the inside cover if needed).

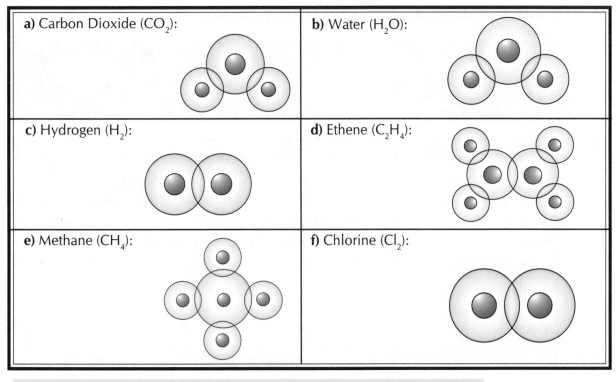

a) Carbon Dioxide (CO_2):

b) Water (H_2O):

c) Hydrogen (H_2):

d) Ethene (C_2H_4):

e) Methane (CH_4):

f) Chlorine (Cl_2):

Q8   Examiners love carbon dioxide and water as examples of covalent bonding.

a)   Fill in the missing words:
Carbon dioxide and water both have _____ melting points. Carbon dioxide is usually found as a _____ and water as a _____. Water and carbon dioxide ____ _____ conduct electricity.

b)   Describe the structure of carbon dioxide and water.
Relate the structure to the properties of the molecules.

Structures

Q1 Below are some examples of giant covalent structures.
Give the names of all the structures below.

a)

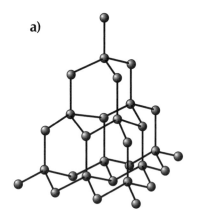

b)

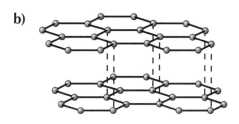

c)

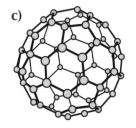

Hint Corner

Bling!
Bling!

Q2 Complete the paragraph below using the words from the list.

slide	soft	hard	no	diamond
atoms	graphite	large	lubricant	high
graphite	diamond	carbon	four	three	layers
delocalised	rigid	strong	one

Giant covalent structures consist of millions of _____ which are held together by covalent
bonds. Due to the _____ number of covalent bonds in their structures, they have _____
melting and boiling points. _____ and _____ are both giant covalent structures
made from _____ . In diamond each carbon atom forms _____ covalent bonds which
leads to a _____ structure of very strong bonds. This makes diamond a very _____
substance. In graphite each carbon atom forms _____ covalent bonds, which means that
graphite consists of _____ of carbon atoms which can _____ over each other. This makes
graphite _____ and ideal as a _____. The atoms in diamond have _____ free electrons
while the atoms in graphite have _____ free, _____ electron. This means that _____
is a conductor but _____ isn't.

Diamond is dead hard — so no messin', right...
Simple molecular compounds have loads of small molecules that are easy to pull away from each other.
Giant covalent structures have <u>one huge molecule</u> containing billions of covalently bonded atoms
— and they're <u>really hard</u> to pull apart. So that's why their properties are so different. Makes sense.

Module CD4 — Carbon Chemistry

Alkanes

Q1   What is the general formula for an alkane?

Q2   Complete the table by filling in the missing information.

Name	Formula	Number of Carbons	Melting Point(°C)	Boiling Point(°C)	Structural Formula
Methane	CH_4	1	-182	-164	H‑C‑H (with H above and below)
Ethane	C_2H_6		-183	-89	H‑C‑C‑H (with H's)
Propane	C_3H_8	3	-190	-42	
Butane	C_4H_{10}	4	-138	0	H‑C‑C‑C‑C‑H (with H's)
Pentane	C_5H_{12}	5	-130	36	H‑C‑C‑C‑C‑C‑H (with H's)
Hexane		6	-95	69	H‑C‑C‑C‑C‑C‑C‑H (with H's)
Heptane	C_7H_{16}	7	-91	99	H‑C‑C‑C‑C‑C‑C‑C‑H (with H's)
Octane		8	-57	126	
Nonane	C_9H_{20}	9	-51	151	H‑C‑C‑C‑C‑C‑C‑C‑C‑C‑H (with H's)
Decane	$C_{10}H_{22}$		-30	174	H‑C‑C‑C‑C‑C‑C‑C‑C‑C‑C‑H (with H's)

Q3   Answer the following:

a)   Alkanes are what type of chemical?

b)   **Explain** what is meant by a 'single covalent bond'.

c)   What does the term '**saturated**' mean?

d)   What is the **result** of a bromine test on an alkane?

e)   A catalyst can be used to break down long alkane molecule chains into smaller, more useful molecules. What is the **name** of this process?

f)   Why does it make more sense to turn unreactive alkanes into **more useful chemicals**, rather than **burn** them?

Top Tips: You break up long hydrocarbons to make them <u>less viscous</u> and, more importantly, to produce <u>alkenes</u>. If you take a long hydrocarbon, and make a shorter one out of it, the bit left over <u>has</u> to be an alkene — or there aren't enough bonds to go round. Remember alkenes have a C=C <u>double bond</u>, and they join up to make <u>polymers</u> — cracking stuff.

Alkenes

Q1   Alkenes are unsaturated hydrocarbons.

  a)   What does **unsaturated** mean?

  b)   Why does this make alkenes **useful**?

Q2   Elements are easily added to alkenes. These reactions are called **addition reactions**.

  a)   **Why** do alkenes so readily undergo addition reactions?

  b)   Ethene can undergo an addition reaction with hydrogen.

  i) Write a symbol equation to show this reaction.

  ii) Draw the structural formulae of the molecules in this reaction.

  iii) What is the name of the **product** formed?

  iv) What are the conditions required for this reaction to take place?

  v) What is the name for this type of reaction?

  c)   Propene undergoes the same reaction. Write a balanced symbol equation for the reaction.

Q3   **Bromine water** can be used to distinguish between ethane and ethene.

  a)   What happens when ethene is mixed with bromine water?

  b)   Write the balanced symbol equation from the formula below.

$$\underset{H}{\overset{H}{>}}C=C\underset{H}{\overset{H}{<}} + Br-Br \longrightarrow H-\underset{\underset{Br}{|}}{\overset{\overset{H}{|}}{C}}-\underset{\underset{Br}{|}}{\overset{\overset{H}{|}}{C}}-H$$

Bromine Water

  c)   Write a balanced symbol equation for the bromination of propene.

  d)   What is the name of the compound that is formed when an alkene reacts with bromine water?

Q4   **Copy and complete** the table below.

Alkene	No. of Carbon atoms	Formula	Structural Formula
Ethene			
Propene			

Top Tips: Alkenes are <u>unsaturated</u> — they have <u>spare bonds</u>, ready to <u>react</u> with other chemicals or make <u>polymers</u>. That makes them a bit more exciting than alkanes but you've still got to learn the <u>names</u> and <u>structural formulae</u>, and get an idea of the <u>physical properties</u>.

Hydrocarbons

Q1   What is **cracking**? Give **two** reasons why it is carried out.

Q2   Look at the diagram on the right.

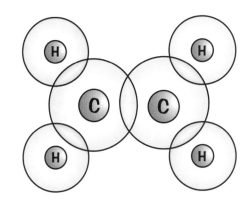

Heat

a) Gas **A** produced in this reaction is an alkene. What are alkenes?

b) Alkenes are **unsaturated**. What does this mean?

c) Paraffin does not decolourise orange/brown bromine water, but gas **A** collected in the gas jar does. **Explain** these observations.

d) **Complete** the equation by filling in the box with the structural formula of A:

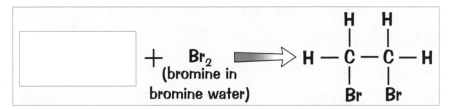

e) Name gas **A**.

Q3   Only the **larger** fractions obtained by the distillation of crude oil are cracked. Why is this?

Q4 $C_{16}H_{34}$ was heated strongly with a catalyst, in the absence of air. This is one reaction that occurred:

$$C_{16}H_{34} \rightarrow 2C_2H_4 + C_6H_{12} + C_6H_{14}$$

a) **Name** the process shown in the equation.

b) Why is this reaction carried out in the **absence** of air?

c) **Which** of these molecules are **unsaturated**?

d) **Which** of them are **saturated**?

e) **Which** molecules would:

i) Decolourise bromine water?

ii) Polymerise?

f) **Complete** the dot and cross diagram on the right, showing the outer electrons in an ethene molecule.

g) **Name** two uses of 'cracked' hydrocarbons.

h) What is made when many molecules of ethene join up?

i) **Name** the molecule that forms when chloroethene polymerises — and give its abbreviation.

Q5   Butane and butene are useful products obtained from cracking octane (C_8H_{18}).

Write down a balanced symbol equation for the cracking of octane.

Polymers and Plastics

Q1   **Explain** what you understand by the term **'polymerisation'**.

Q2   Ethene can undergo many addition reactions to form long chain polymers. What **reaction conditions** are necessary for this to happen?

Q3   Lots of ethene molecules can join together to form a substance that is useful.

    a)   What is this polymer **called**?

    b)   Using the ethene molecule shown on the right to help you, **draw** a diagram to show how the monomers of ethene form their polymer.

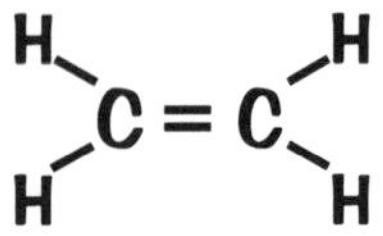

    c)   **Explain** the naming of ethene's polymer.

Q4   **Complete** the paragraph below by filling in the missing words, using each word once.

ethene monomers   ethene   carbon   catalyst   polythene   polymerisation
double bonds   monomer   polymer   plastics   addition   single   high pressure

_____ is the formation of long chain _____ molecules from the _____ of single monomer units. The type of atoms in the _____ gives the _____ its properties. _____ are made from these long chain hydrocarbons. _____ is made from the monomer _____. _____ _____ are brought together at _____ _____ over a heated _____. The _____ _____ are broken, forming two _____ covalent bonds.

Q5   Other alkenes can also break their double bond to form long-chain polymers.

    Complete the diagram below.

Monomer	Name	Polymer	Name
a) 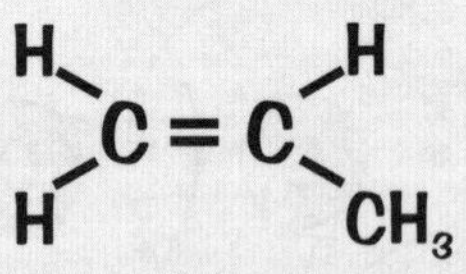 $H_2C=CHCH_3$	Propene		
	Styrene	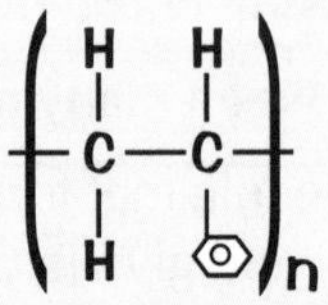	
c) 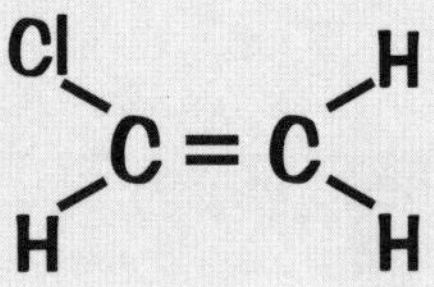 $ClHC=CH_2$	Chloroethene		

Uses of Plastics

Q1 Using the information given in the first table below, decide which polymer you think would be **most suitable** for the jobs below. Fill your answers in the second table:

We bring you Gold, Frankincense... and poly-myrrh

Polymer	Some properties
1) Polystyrene	Cheap, easily moulded, can be expanded into foam.
2) Polythene	Cheap, strong, easy to mould.
3) Polypropene	Forms strong fibres, highly elastic.
4) PTFE	Hard, waxy, things do not stick to it.
5) Perspex	Transparent, easily moulded, does not easily shatter.

Job	Plastic	Reason
a) Hot food container		
b) Plastic bags		
c) Carpet		
d) Picnic glasses		
e) Buckets		
f) Ropes		
g) Bubble packing		
h) Insulating material		
i) Yoghurt cartons		
j) Non-stick frying pans		

Q2 What is the name of a family of polymers that can be used as adhesives?

Q3 There are a lot of environmental issues that surround the use of plastics.
Try to list as many as you can.

Q4 What type of bonds hold the atoms together in plastics?

Q5 How does the strength of the bonds in a plastic affect its properties?

Top Tips: Plastics are widely used in the modern world and are a useful product of polymerisation. Unfortunately they're also quite dull. You need to know all their properties and what it is that gives them their properties — these questions will help you learn them.

Chemical Equations

You won't get anywhere with chemistry without getting used to equations.
They look horrible at first — but you'll be fine with a little practice...

Q1   **Complete** the following **word** equations:

a)   Sodium   +   chlorine   →   _____ _____

b)   Carbon   +   _____   →   Carbon dioxide

c)   Sulphur   +   oxygen   →   _____ _____

d)   Zinc   +   oxygen   →   _____ _____

e)   _____   +   _____   →   Iron sulphide

f)   Potassium + chlorine →   _____ _____

g)   Lead + oxygen →   _____ _____

h)   _____   +   _____   →   Calcium oxide

Q2   **Complete** the following **word** equations:

a) Iron	+	sulphur	→
b) Iron	+	oxygen	→
c) Magnesium	+	oxygen	→
d) Sulphur	+	oxygen	→
e) Hydrogen	+	oxygen	→
f) Magnesium	+	sulphur	→
g) Aluminium	+	chlorine	→
h) Hydrogen	+	iodine	→
i) Carbon	+	oxygen	→

Q3   Look at the following **equation**:

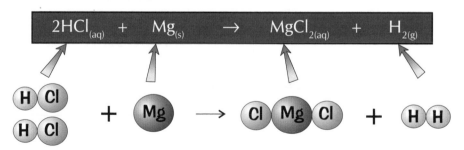

a)   What do the symbols (g), (aq) and (s) mean?

b)   What other **similar symbol** is used? What does it **represent**?

__Balancing Equations__

Q1   Write out the **symbol** equations for these word equations:

a)   Carbon + oxygen   carbon dioxide

b)   Zinc + sulphuric acid   zinc sulphate + hydrogen

c)   Copper + chlorine   copper chloride

d)   Hydrogen + copper oxide   copper + water

e)   Magnesium + sulphuric acid   magnesium sulphate + hydrogen

Q2   **Balance** the following equations by putting the correct numbers before the formulae.

a) N_2 + H_2 $\rightarrow$ NH_3

b) $CaCO_3$ + H_2SO_4 $\rightarrow$ $CaSO_4$ + H_2O + CO_2

c) H_2 + O_2 $\rightarrow$ H_2O

d) Mg + O_2 $\rightarrow$ MgO

e) Mg + H_2SO_4 $\rightarrow$ $MgSO_4$ + H_2

f) H_2SO_4 + $NaOH$ $\rightarrow$ Na_2SO_4 + H_2O

g) Ca + H_2SO_4 $\rightarrow$ $CaSO_4$ + H_2

h) H_2SO_4 + KOH $\rightarrow$ K_2SO_4 + H_2O

And more...

i) Fe_2O_3 + CO $\rightarrow$ Fe + CO_2

j) $C_6H_{12}O_6$ + O_2 $\rightarrow$ CO_2 + H_2O

k) CO_2 + H_2O $\rightarrow$ $C_6H_{12}O_6$ + O_2

l) C_4H_{10} + O_2 $\rightarrow$ CO_2 + H_2O

m) C_2H_4 + O_2 $\rightarrow$ CO_2 + H_2O

n) C_3H_8 + O_2 $\rightarrow$ CO_2 + H_2O

o) C_5H_{12} + O_2 $\rightarrow$ CO_2 + H_2O

p) C_3H_6 + O_2 $\rightarrow$ CO_2 + H_2O

q) C_2H_6 + O_2 $\rightarrow$ CO_2 + H_2O

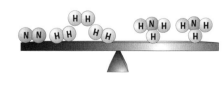

__Right lad, you need six of one and half a dozen of t'other...__

Check each element, then check them again. Keep checking till nothing needs changing, then it's got to be right. But <u>don't change</u> the numbers <u>inside</u> the formulae — that would completely change the reaction.

__Relative Formula Mass__

Example: Find the **relative atomic mass** (A$_r$) of zinc.
(Which is basically the same as asking....
"Find the mass of one **mole** of zinc.")

> Look on the Periodic Table (at the front of the book)
> for the relative atomic mass of zinc, which is 65.
>
> __Answer__ = __65__   (add a "g" for grams if it asked for a mole.)

Q1   Find the **relative atomic mass** of...

a)   Calcium (Ca)   b)   Sodium (Na)   c)   Iron (Fe)

d)   Chlorine (Cl)   e)   Aluminium (Al)   f)   Mercury (Hg)

Example: Find the **relative formula mass** (M$_r$) of zinc oxide.
(Which is basically the same as asking....
"Find the mass of one **mole** of zinc oxide.")

> Zinc oxide has a formula ZnO. ie. 1 zinc atom and 1 oxygen atom, so
> add up the masses of these atoms:
>
> $$(1 \times Zn) + (1 \times O) \quad = (1 \times 65) + (1 \times 16)$$
> $$= \quad 65 \quad + \quad 16$$
> $$= \quad \underline{81}$$
>
> (Then put a "g" for grams
> if it asked for a mole.)

Q2   Find the **relative formula mass** of ...

a)   Hydrogen molecules (H$_2$)   b)   Oxygen molecules (O$_2$)   c)   Chlorine molecules (Cl$_2$)

d)   Bromine molecules (Br$_2$)   e)   Nitrogen molecules (N$_2$)   f)   Fluorine molecules (F$_2$)

Q3   Calculate the **relative formula mass** of the following compounds:

a)   Copper oxide (CuO)   b)   Hydrogen chloride (HCl)   c)   Sodium chloride (NaCl)

d)   Carbon monoxide (CO)   e)   Sodium bromide (NaBr)   f)   Lithium iodide (LiI)

Q4   Calculate the **relative formula mass** of these more complex compounds:

a)   Carbon dioxide (CO$_2$)   b)   Water (H$_2$O)   c)   Ethene (C$_2$H$_4$)

d)   Barium sulphate (BaSO$_4$)   e)   Aluminium oxide (Al$_2$O$_3$)   f)   Lead iodide (PbI$_2$)

Q5   And finally these **hideously** complex compounds:

a)   Potassium manganate(VII) (KMnO$_4$)   b)   Tetrachloromethane (CCl$_4$)

c)   Citric acid (C$_6$H$_8$O$_7$)   d)   Calcium hydroxide (Ca(OH)$_2$)

e)   Potassium dichromate (K$_2$Cr$_2$O$_7$)   f)   Lead nitrate (Pb(NO$_3$)$_2$)

Percentage Element in a Compound

Calculations = loads of easy marks once you've got them sussed. Read on to find out how...

Remember this formula:

$$\% \text{ Mass of an element in a compound} = \frac{A_r \times \text{No. of atoms (of that element)}}{M_r \text{ (of whole compound)}} \times 100\%$$

(Remember: A_r = Relative Atomic Mass; M_r = Relative Molecular Mass)

Here's an example worked out for you:

Find the % mass of sodium in Na_2SO_4.

$$\frac{A_r \times n}{M_r} \times 100: \qquad \frac{23 \times 2}{142} \times 100 \qquad = \qquad \underline{32.4\%}$$

(Remember: n is the number of atoms of the element you're interested in.)

Q1 Using the Periodic Table at the front of this book, find the % mass of the specified elements in these compounds:

a) the % carbon in CO_2
b) the % carbon in CO
c) the % potassium in KCl
d) the % sodium in NaF
e) the % copper in CuO
f) the % sulphur in SO_2
g) the % oxygen in SO_2
h) the % sulphur in SO_3
i) the % oxygen in SO_3
j) the % hydrogen in H_2O

k) the % nitrogen in NH_3
l) the % sodium in $NaOH$
m) the % water in $CuSO_4.5H_2O$
n) the % aluminium in Al_2O_3
o) the % copper in $CuCO_3$
p) the % copper in $CuSO_4$
q) the % potassium in KNO_3
r) the % phosphorus in $(NH_4)_3PO_4$
s) the % nitrogen in NH_4NO_3
t) the % nitrogen in $(NH_4)_2SO_4$

Q2 Which has the greatest % mass of carbon? Show how you **calculated** your answer.

a) CH_4 b) C_6H_6 c) C_2H_5OH

Q3 Which has the greater % **mass** of aluminium? Show your working.

a) Al_2O_3 b) Na_3AlF_6

Q4 Which of these iron ores has the most iron in it by **percentage mass**?

a) Siderite ($FeCO_3$)   b) Haematite (Fe_2O_3)   c) Magnetite (Fe_3O_4)   d) Iron pyrite (FeS_2)

Q5 Calculate the % **mass** of **metal** in:

a) $NaCl$ b) $MgCO_3$ c) Zn d) KOH

Empirical Formulae

Empirical formulae show the ratios of the different kinds of atom in a substance.

Look at the example below:

A compound contains 75g carbon and 25g hydrogen. What is its empirical formula?

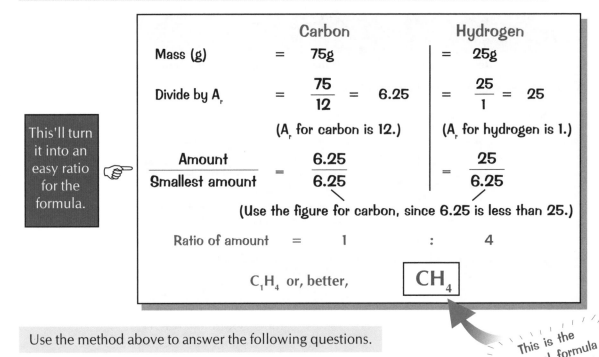

This'll turn it into an easy ratio for the formula.

	Carbon	Hydrogen
Mass (g)	= 75g	= 25g
Divide by A_r	$= \dfrac{75}{12} = 6.25$	$= \dfrac{25}{1} = 25$
	(A_r for carbon is 12.)	(A_r for hydrogen is 1.)
$\dfrac{\text{Amount}}{\text{Smallest amount}}$	$= \dfrac{6.25}{6.25}$	$= \dfrac{25}{6.25}$

(Use the figure for carbon, since 6.25 is less than 25.)

Ratio of amount = 1 : 4

C_1H_4 or, better, $\boxed{CH_4}$

This is the empirical formula

Q1   Use the method above to answer the following questions.

a)   2.70g of aluminium is combined with 10.65g of chlorine.
What is the **empirical formula**?

b)   1.6g of sulphur was heated in oxygen. Its mass increased to 4.0g.
What is the **name** of this oxide of sulphur?

c)   1.48g of a calcium compound contains 0.8g of calcium,
0.64g of oxygen and 0.04g of hydrogen. **Name** the compound.

d)   Copper sulphate crystals contain **water of crystallisation** (water in its crystal structure) and have
the formula $CuSO_4 \cdot xH_2O$, where x is a number. 49.9g of a sample of copper sulphate was found
to have 18g of water of crystallisation. **Calculate x.**

If you're given the **% mass** of the elements in the compound rather than the **actual masses**, just
assume you have **100g** of the compound. So 80% carbon and 20% hydrogen would mean
using 80g carbon and 20g hydrogen in the method above. **Do everything else the same.**

Q2   Find the empirical formula of the following:

a)   A hydrocarbon of 80% carbon, 20% hydrogen.

b)   Cryolite, (an aluminium ore used in
the extraction of aluminium from
bauxite), containing 33% sodium, 13%
aluminium, and 54% fluorine.

c)   A compound of 82% nitrogen,
18% hydrogen.

d)   Nitram (an ammonium fertiliser
containing 35% nitrogen, 5%
hydrogen and 60% oxygen).

Empirical — my Dear Watson...

Empirical formulae are **not** the same thing as real (molecular) formulae — you've got to cancel those
numbers. So, ethene's molecular formula is C_2H_4, but its empirical formula is CH_2 — you're writing the
ratio of the numbers of moles in its simplest form.

Calculating Masses in Reactions

Q1 Answer the following questions about this equation: Fe + S   FeS

a) What mass of **sulphur** is needed to react with 56g of iron?

b) What mass of **sulphur** is needed to react with 5.6g of iron?

c) **Work out** the mass of **iron sulphide** produced when
5.6g of iron completely reacts with excess sulphur.

d) **Calculate** the mass of **iron sulphide** produced when 320g of sulphur is reacted with excess iron.

e) **Calculate** the mass of iron required to make 88g of **iron sulphide** by reacting iron with sulphur.

Q2 The decomposition of calcium carbonate is given by the equation:
$$CaCO_3 \quad CaO + CO_2$$
Calculate the mass of carbon dioxide that is released when the
following masses of calcium carbonate **decompose** on heating:

a) 100g

b) 20g

Q3 Answer the following question about this reaction:
$$Fe_2O_3 + 3CO \rightarrow 2Fe + 3CO_2$$
What **mass** of iron would be obtained from 160 tonnes of iron(III) oxide?

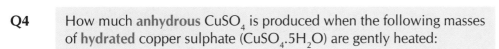

Iron ore, coke and limestone

1500°C

Hot air

Molten iron   Molten slag

Q4 How much **anhydrous** $CuSO_4$ is produced when the following masses
of **hydrated** copper sulphate ($CuSO_4.5H_2O$) are gently heated:

a) 250g?

b) 12.5g?

Q5 Answer the following question about this reaction: $2Al_2O_3 \rightarrow 4Al + 3O_2$

How much aluminium oxide would be needed to make the following **masses** of aluminium:

a) 108kg?   **b)** 1kg?   **c)** 5kg?   **d)** 1 tonne (1 tonne = 1000kg)?

Q6 Copper oxide can be **reduced** to copper using methane.
The reaction follows the equation: $4CuO + CH_4 \quad 4Cu + CO_2 + 2H_2O$

How much copper oxide would be needed to make the following masses of copper:

a) 25.6g ?   **b)** 19.2g ?

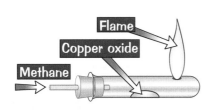

Flame

Copper oxide

Methane

21st century mole

Simple Reversible Reactions

Q1 Study pictures **A** , **B** and **C** carefully.

a) **Complete** the following passage using the words given in the box.
Use each word once only.

equilibrium	open	upwards	downwards	dynamic	balanced
activity	change	static	closed	equilibrium	dynamic

Picture **A** shows a see-saw which is perfectly _____ and not moving. It is in _____. This type of _____ is said to be _____. Picture **B** shows a different type of equilibrium. The escalator is moving _____, whilst the man is trying to walk _____. There is constant _____, but no _____ in overall position. This is _____ equilibrium. All reversible reactions are examples of _____ equilibrium. Dynamic equilibria always occur in _____ systems, where nothing can escape or get into the system. An _____ system is like a jar with the lid off — things can escape.

b) Picture **C** shows a bottle of pop. **What type** of equilibrium exists between the carbon dioxide dissolved in the drink and that in the air above it?

c) What type of **system** does C represent?

d) If the top were removed, what type of **system** would you have? What would happen to the equilibrium?

Q2 Look at the graph opposite.

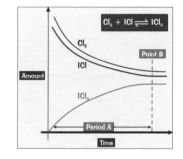

a) What is happening to the reactants during **period A**?

b) What has happened at **point B**?

c) What type of **equilibrium** is this?

Q3 Consider the reaction: $N_2O_{4 (g)} \rightleftharpoons 2NO_{2 (g)}$

Suggest what would happen to the equilibrium if you:

a) increased the **temperature**.

b) increased the **pressure**.

c) doubled the **concentration** of N_2O_4.

For the forward reaction, ΔH is +ve (it's an endothermic reaction)

Q4 The equation $N_{2 (g)} + 3H_{2 (g)} \rightleftharpoons 2NH_{3 (g)}$ describes the Haber Process.

Suggest what would happen to the position of equilibrium if you:

a) increased the **pressure**.   c) added more **nitrogen**.

b) increased the **temperature**.   d) removed the **ammonia**.

For the forward reaction, ΔH is -ve (it's an exothermic reaction)

Top Tips: If two things can <u>combine</u>, they can <u>separate</u> — <u>any</u> reaction's basically reversible. Usually, though, one way's <u>much faster</u> than the other, so you don't notice. If you can picture what's happening at the <u>molecular</u> level, you're much more likely to <u>remember</u> it... probably.

Yield and Cost of Production

Q1   The diagram opposite shows the Haber Process.

a)   Write a fully **balanced equation** for the reaction, including state symbols.

b)   What **catalyst** is used?

c)   What is the **function** of the catalyst?

d)   Why are **fine pellets** used?

e)   Use the information on the graph to suggest the **optimum conditions** for ammonia production.

f)   **Explain** why high pressures are used.

g)   The conditions actually used are 450°C and 200 atm pressure.
Explain why this lower pressure and higher temperature are used.

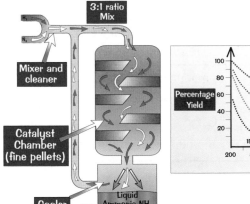

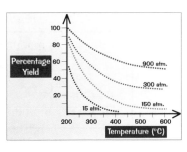

Q2   The equation $2SO_{2\ (g)} + O_{2\ (g)} \rightleftharpoons 2SO_{3\ (g)}$ describes the Contact Process for making sulphuric acid.

The forward reaction is exothermic (ΔH is -ve)

a)   What is the effect on the position of equilibrium of increasing: (i) **temperature** (ii) **pressure**?

b)   **Suggest** the optimum conditions that could be used for a high yield.

c)   The actual operating temperature is relatively high despite a poor yield (see graph).
What does this optimise?

d)   In this process 100% conversion could be achieved using extremely high pressures of around 1000 atm. Suggest a reason why this pressure is **not** used commercially.

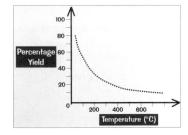

Q3   A factory manufactures ammonium nitrate. The table below shows the predicted mass and the actual mass of fertiliser made.

Predicted Mass	Actual Mass
160 tonnes	144 tonnes

What is the **percentage yield** of ammonium nitrate obtained?

Q4   A mining company has to consider a number of questions before it starts mining a site.
Place these points in the order you think the mining company is most likely to consider them.

a)   How much of the metal is there?

b)   Is there a workforce nearby?

c)   Is there transport nearby?

d)   Is there a local supply of cheap electricity?

e)   Is there a saleable metal there?

Q5   What are the **advantages** of using catalysts in the industrial manufacture of chemicals?

Ammonia and Fertilisers

Q1 **Complete** the following paragraphs by filling in the missing words from the list below. You may use the words once, more than once or not at all.

450	1000	ammonia	atom	hydrogen	nitrogen	atoms	
200	fertilisers	unreacted	Haber Process	recycled	pressure		

_____ is manufactured by the _____ _____. One use for ammonia is in the making of _____. The gases _____ and _____ are brought together under the special conditions of _____ °C and a _____ of _____ atm. Nothing is wasted — any _____ gas is _____ . Hydrogen and nitrogen combine in a ratio of 3 _____ of _____ to 1 _____ of _____ .

Q2 The reaction that produces ammonia is shown below:

Nitrogen + Hydrogen $\rightleftharpoons$ Ammonia

$$N_2 + 3H_2 \rightleftharpoons 2NH_3$$

a) The forward reaction is **exothermic**. What does this mean?

b) If you **increase the temperature**, what will happen to the yield of ammonia?

c) The yield at a lower temperature is higher, yet the temperature chosen for this process is high. **Explain** why such a high temperature is chosen.

d) A high pressure will give an increased yield and an increase in the rate of reaction. **Explain** this statement in terms of particles, gases and the collision theory.

Q3 Ammonia is made into ammonium nitrate in three main stages. Firstly, the ammonia needs to be converted into nitrogen monoxide.

Step 1 $$NH_{3(g)} + 5O_{2(g)} \rightarrow 4NO_{(g)} + H_2O_{(l)}$$

a) **Balance** this equation and state the **products** made in the reaction.

Step 2 $$NO_{(g)} + 3O_{2\,(g)} + H_2O_{(g)} \rightarrow HNO_{3(aq)}$$

b) **Balance** the equation.

c) Name the product formed in this reaction.

Step 3   Nitric acid then needs to be converted into ammonium nitrate.

d) Write a **word equation** and **balanced symbol equation** for this reaction.

e) What **type** of reaction is this?

f) Ammonium nitrate is a fertiliser. Which **element** in ammonium nitrate is particularly useful for plants? What do plants **use** this element for?

Ammonia and Fertilisers

Q4   The two gases used to make ammonia in the Haber Process are hydrogen and nitrogen.

a)   **Where** does the nitrogen come from?

b)   Not all the nitrogen and hydrogen end up as ammonia.
Why is this and **how** is it compensated for?

Q5   Ammonia compounds make good inorganic fertilisers.

a)   Name **three** nitrogenous fertilisers.

b)   What **property** of these makes them useful as a fertiliser?

c)   Why can this property be a **problem** from time to time?

Q6   Ammonium sulphate is also used as a fertiliser. It is manufactured using the ammonia from the Haber Process and the sulphuric acid from the Contact Process.

a)   The reaction between ammonia and sulphuric acid to make ammonium sulphate is an **example** of what type of reaction?

b)   Write a **word equation** for this reaction.

c)   Write a balanced **symbol equation** for this reaction.

Q7   The sentences below are steps in a lake becoming **eutrophic**, but they are muddled up.

a)   **Sort** them into the correct order and write them down.

b)   In the corrected sequence, **why** should water plants grow more quickly?

c)   What **resources** are the water plants competing for? Which resource is probably in excess?

d)   If there are more plants in the lake, you might expect **more oxygen** to be produced by photosynthesis. Why does the oxygen content of the water go **down** instead?

- Fish and other aquatic animals die of suffocation.
- The microbes take more oxygen from the water for their respiration.
- Excess fertilisers leach from the soil and are washed into the lake.
- The number of microbes that feed on dead organisms increases.
- There is increased competition between the plants, and some die as a result.
- Water plants in the lake start to grow rapidly.

Normally, the action of decomposers such as bacteria is welcomed because it allows scarce nutrients to be recycled for use by other organisms in the community, as in the nitrogen cycle.

e)   Why is the action of decomposers such a **problem** in the case of a eutrophic lake?

Fertilise your mind — with this page...

Fertilisers are needed to provide important <u>nutrients</u> for <u>plants</u>, particularly food crops. Don't forget the ways that nitrate fertilisers can <u>pollute</u> the water, and what farmers can do to <u>reduce</u> this problem.

Acids and Bases

Q1 **Decide** whether the following statements are true or false.

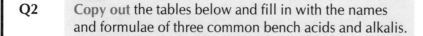

a) All acids are dangerous.

b) All bases are dangerous.

c) Acids produce H^+ ions in solution.

d) Alkalis produce OH^- ions in solution.

e) Acids have a pH above 7.

f) Acids have a pH below 7.

g) The pH scale goes from 1 to 14.

Q2 **Copy out** the tables below and fill in with the names and formulae of three common bench acids and alkalis.

Name of Acid	Formula of Acid
(i)	
(ii)	
(iii)	

Name of Alkali	Formula of Alkali
(i)	
(ii)	
(iii)	

Q3 What do we call a substance with a **pH** of 7? Give an **example** of a substance whose pH is 7.

Q4 State which of the following are **acids** and which are **bases**:

a) Hydrochloric acid   b) Sodium hydroxide   c) KOH

d) H_2SO_4 e) HNO_3

Q5 Answer the following:

a) What is an **alkali**?   b) What is a **base**?   c) Give a definition of a **salt**.

Q6 Copy the pH chart below. Then colour it in with the **correct colours** for Universal Indicator solution:

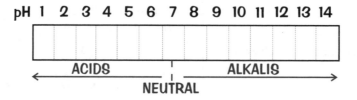

Q7 What **pH values** would you expect for...

a) Citric acid ?   d) Oven cleaner?

b) Sodium chloride (common salt)?   e) Sodium hydroxide?

c) Lime (calcium hydroxide)?   f) Hydrochloric acid?

Acids and Bases

Q8   The labels have fallen off test tubes of vinegar, water, sulphuric acid, and oven cleaner. The table on the right shows the colours observed when pH paper was added to each tube.

Fill in the missing **pH values** and **identify** which substance is in which tube.

Tube	Colour	pH
1	Red	
2	Orange	
3	Green	
4	Blue	

Q9   **Link up** the words in the diagram opposite to show the salt produced by each acid.

Sulphuric acid		Nitrates
Hydrochloric acid		Sulphates
Nitric acid		Chlorides

Q10   Write out the **products** of the following reactions. Then write the **formulae** for the compounds, and **balance** the equation. There's an example completed for you:

hydrochloric acid + sodium hydroxide → sodium chloride + water

HCl + $NaOH$ → $NaCl$ + H_2O

sulphuric acid + potassium hydroxide →

hydrochloric acid + calcium carbonate →

nitric acid + ammonia   →

Q11   Complete the following reaction by filling in the missing product.

acid + base →   salt + _____

Q12   Neutralisation is simplified as $H^+_{(aq)} + OH^-_{(aq)} \rightarrow H_2O_{(l)}$.
Explain where the H^+ and OH^- come from.

Q13   Calcium hydroxide is used to neutralise farm land.

What **kind of substance** is calcium hydroxide?

Q14   Use the information opposite to **suggest** the best remedy for:

a)   A wasp sting.

b)   A bee sting.

c)   Nettle sting.

> Wasp stings are basic.
> Bee stings are acidic.
> Nettles stings are acidic.
> Bicarbonate of soda is alkaline.
> Dock leaves contain alkali.
> Lemon juice is acidic.

Atoms

Q1   Answer these questions on atoms:

   a)   What is an **atom**?

   b)   **How many** different types of subatomic particles make up an atom?

   c)   What are their **names**?

   d)   What is a **nucleus**?

   e)   What is an **electron shell**?

Q2   Copy the diagram opposite, and complete the labels A, B and C.

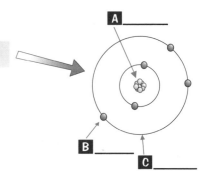

Q3   **Copy and complete** the table below:

Particle	Mass	Charge	Where it is found
Proton	1	+1	
Electron		-1	
Neutron			In the nucleus

Q4   More details on atoms:

   a)   Where is most of the mass in an atom **concentrated**?

   b)   What is between the **nucleus** and the **electrons**?

Q5   Nuclear reactions affect the nucleus. What do **chemical reactions** affect?

Q6   All atoms are neutral. If an atom has seven electrons then **how many** protons does it have?

Q7   Answer these questions on the atomic number and mass number of an element:

   a)   What does the **atomic number** tell us?

   b)   What does the **mass number** tell us?

   c)   What do the letters **A** and **Z** in the diagram stand for? What is **A** minus **Z**?

   d)   How many **protons** are there in an atom of lithium?

   e)   How many **electrons** are there in an atom of lithium?

   f)   How many **neutrons** are there in an atom of lithium?

   g)   **Which number** (mass or atomic) determines what element an atom is?

$$A \searrow^{7}$$
$$\text{Li}$$
$$Z \searrow^{3}$$

Q8   **Calculate** the number of protons, electrons and neutrons in the following:

   a)   Carbon ($^{12}_{6}\text{C}$)   **b)**   Potassium ($^{39}_{19}\text{K}$)   **c)**   Hydrogen ($^{1}_{1}\text{H}$).

Q9   Some questions on isotopes:

   a)   What are **isotopes**? Give an **example** of an isotope used in dating old objects.

   b)   Uranium 235 and Uranium 238 are isotopes. Are they **chemically** different? **Explain** why.

> ## *Top Tips:*   Some tricky new terms here — that's science for you. Make sure you know the
> difference between atomic number and mass number. Come the exam it'll be easy marks...

The Periodic Table

The Periodic Table is great — love it like you love your mother.

Q1 The Periodic Table is very useful. How much do you know about it?

a) In the Periodic Table, what is meant by a **Group**?

b) In the Periodic Table, what is meant by a **Period**?

c) Roughly **how many** elements are there?

d) In what **order** are the elements listed?

e) What might be **similar** about members of the same group?

f) What might be **similar** about members of the same period?

g) If an element is in Group 1 then **how many** electrons will it have in its outer electron shell?

h) If an ion has a 1- charge, then **which group** is that element most likely to be in?

Q2 In this Periodic Table, some elements are shown as letters. They're **not** the correct symbols for the elements. Use the letters to answer the questions.

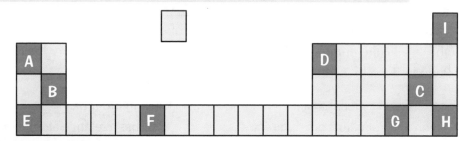

WHICH ELEMENT(S).........

a) are Noble gases?

b) are Halogens?

c) is in Group 2?

d) is in the same period as C?

e) has three electrons in its outer shell?

f) has an atomic number of 3?

g) are non-metals?

h) is a transition element?

i) would form an ion with a charge of 1$^+$?

j) will not form an ion easily?

k) would form an ion by gaining 2 electrons per atom?

l) would form an ion with as many electrons as an atom of the element marked I?

m) are the least reactive of those marked in the table?

Q3 A row in the Periodic Table is called a **Period**. As you go down each column, what does each **new Period represent**?

☐ an extra electron   ☐ an extra full shell of electrons   ☐ one fewer shell of electrons.

Module CD6 — The Periodic Table

The Periodic Table

Aaahh... the Periodic Table — everyone's favourite. This is good old-fashioned chemistry at its very best. Or put it another way, this is 21st century OCR Science at its most important...

Q4 Some nice easy questions to test your knowledge of the Periodic Table:

a) Many Periodic Tables have a **zig-zag** line on them dividing metals from non-metals.

i) Where are the **metals** in the Periodic Table in relation to this line?

ii) Where are the **non-metals** in the Periodic Table in relation to this line?

b) Where are the **transition metals** found on the Periodic Table?

c) Which is the **most reactive** member of Group 1?

Q5 Complete the following paragraphs to explain how the Periodic Table is organised. Use the words in the box below.

potassium	protons	relative atomic mass	argon	atomic number

The Periodic Table lists all the elements in order of _____. This means that the smaller the number of _____ an element has, the nearer the top of the Periodic Table it is listed.

In most cases, this means that the elements are also listed in order of _____. But Argon and Potassium are different — _____ has a relative atomic mass of 40, but is listed before _____, which has a relative atomic mass of 39.

Q6 Name one property which is shared by each metal in Group 2 of the Periodic Table.

Q7 Sodium has an atomic number of 11 and a mass number of 23.

Explain in as much detail as you can what this tells us about an atom of sodium.

Q8 Look at the following: Sodium $^{23}_{11}$**Na**, Magnesium $^{24}_{12}$**Mg** .

a) **Draw** an atom of Sodium and Magnesium.
How many electrons does each have to **lose** to achieve a full shell?

b) Use your diagrams from part **a)** to decide which **Period** Magnesium is in. How did you tell?

c) Looking at the atomic structure of these metals, why is Magnesium **less reactive** than Sodium?

Top Tips: The only way to get this stuff right is to sit down with the Periodic Table and work out what's going on. You need to know what the little numbers mean, which are metals / non-metals and what Groups and Periods are. Sounds like paradise — I'm sure you can't wait to get learning...

Electron Shells

Q1   Answer these atom questions:

a)   What **attracts** the electrons to the nucleus?

b)   Give **another** name for an electron orbit.

Q2   **Complete** the table to show the sizes of the electron shells.

Electron shell	Maximum number of electrons in the shell
1st	
2nd	
3rd	

Q3   **Complete** the table below showing the properties of the first 20 elements.
(You will need the Periodic Table at the front of the book.)

Element	Symbol	Atomic Number	Mass Number	Number of Protons	Number of Electrons	Number of Neutrons	Electronic Configuration	Group Number
Hydrogen	H	1	1	1	1	0	1	—
Helium	He	2	4	2	2	2	2	8
Lithium	Li						2, 1	1
Beryllium								2
Boron				5				
Carbon								
Nitrogen		7						
Oxygen					8			
Fluorine							2, 7	
Neon								
Sodium		11						1
Magnesium								
Aluminium		13	27	13	13	14	2, 8, 3	3
Silicon								
Phosphorus								
Sulphur	S							
Chlorine								
Argon								
Potassium								
Calcium						20		2

Q4   Look at the table and answer these questions:

a)   What is the link between **Group number** and **number of outer electrons**?

b)   What is the link between the **Noble gases** (group 8) and **full outer shells**?

c)   Iodine is in Group 7 — **how many** electrons does it have in its outer electron shell?

d)   Xenon is in Group 8 — **how many** electrons does it have in its outer electron shell?

e)   The **number of electrons** in the outer shell governs which **properties** of the element?

Q5   An atom of element X has two outer electrons that do not fill the outer shell.

a)   Name its **group**.

b)   Is it a **metal** or **non-metal**?

c)   Name **an element** with similar chemical properties to X.

Electron Shells

Electron arrangement is easy. In fact it's very easy. All you need to remember is that the first shell can hold two, while shells 2 and 3 can hold eight. Then just fill 'em up...

Q6 Copy out the diagrams below. Complete them using crosses to show the **full electron arrangement** — and write it down in numbers too. The first three have been done for you.

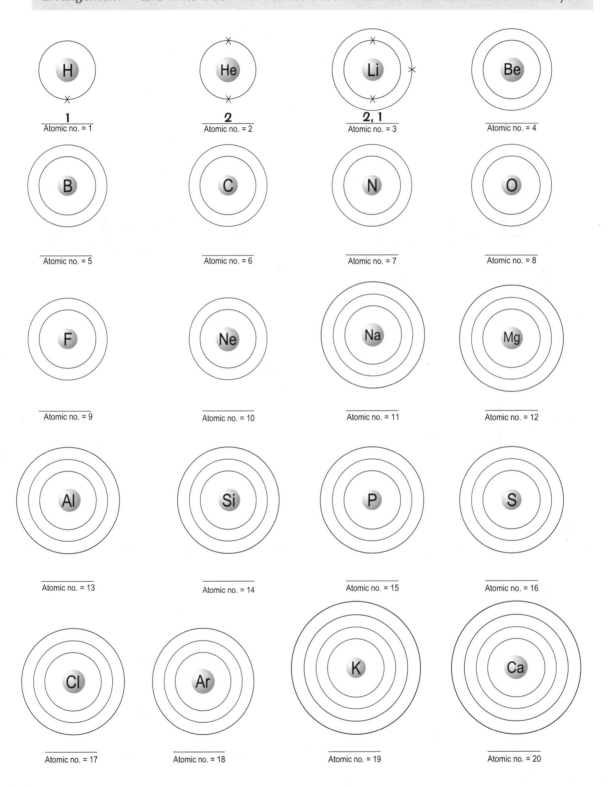

Top-tips: In Exams they're always asking you to draw out electron arrangements, or "configurations". Make sure you can work them out from atomic numbers or the Periodic Table. If you're lucky, they might only ask you to draw the outer shell — easy or what. Bet you can't wait...

Ions

Ions are dead simple — they've got a bit of charge, that's all...

Q1 **Draw out** these ions. Remember Group I elements make 1⁺ ions and Group 2 elements make 2⁺ ions.

  a) Potassium, **b)** Magnesium, **c)** Calcium, **d)** Aluminium.

Q2 **Draw out** these ions. Remember Group 7 elements make 1⁻ ions and Group 6 elements make 2⁻ ions.

  a) Fluoride, **b)** Chloride, **c)** Sulphide.

Q3 Will the **charge** on the following ions be positive or negative?

  a) A metal or hydrogen ion.
  b) A non-metal ion.

Q4 Answer these questions covering some of the basics of ionic bonding:

  a) Why do sodium ions have a **1⁺ charge**?
  b) Why do chloride ions have a **1⁻ charge**?
  c) What charge would you find on a **Group 2 ion**?
  d) What charge would you find on a **Group 6 ion**?
  e) Why is it rare to find a **4⁺ ion** of carbon?

Ionic substances are tough but brittle — don't push them too far.

Q5 **Draw** electron configuration diagrams (only draw the outermost shell) to show what happens in the following reactions.

  a) A sodium atom reacting with a chlorine atom. **Name** the compound formed.
  b) A magnesium atom reacting with two chlorine atoms.

Q6 **Draw** a picture to show the positions of sodium and chloride ions in a sodium chloride crystal.

Q7 **Name** the following ions:

  a) Na^+ **b)** O^{2-} **c)** S^{2-} **d)** NO_3^- **e)** SO_4^{2-} **f)** I^- **g)** F^- **h)** K^+ **i)** Ca^{2+} **j)** Mg^{2+} **k)** PO_4^{3-} **l)** H^+

Q8 Give the **formulae** of magnesium oxide, sodium fluoride, sodium oxide, magnesium sulphate and sodium sulphate. Use the ions from the last question to help you.

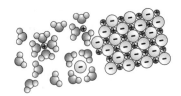

Q9 Why do ionic substances only **conduct electricity** when molten or when dissolved in water?

Q10 Which in the following list are **general** properties of an ionically bonded compound?

  a) High boiling point.
  b) Usually dissolve in water.
  c) Conductor when solid.
  d) Non-conductor when melted.
  e) Weak forces hold molecules together.
  f) Non-crystalline.

Symbols, Formulae and Equations

Q1   Write out the chemical symbols for the following:

Iron   Lead   Zinc   Tin   Copper

Q2   Copy and complete this table:

Name	Formula	Number of atoms of each element present in one particle
Zinc oxide	ZnO	1 zinc 1 oxygen
Magnesium oxide	MgO	
Sodium chloride	NaCl	
	CO_2	1 carbon 2 oxygen
	NaOH	1 sodium 1 oxygen 1 hydrogen
Potassium hydroxide		
	$MgCl_2$	
	H_2	
		2 Chlorine

Q3   Complete the following:

When **chlorine** reacts with a metal to make an ionic compound it forms a **chlor**_____.

When **oxygen** reacts with a metal to make an ionic compound it forms an **ox**_____.

When **sulphur** reacts with a metal to make an ionic compound it forms a **sulph**_____.

Q4   Sodium chloride is made into a solution before it is electrolysed.

a)   What is this **solution** called?

b)   Why does sodium chloride have to be made into a **solution** before electrolysis?

Q5   Complete the following sentences by **filling in** the missing words (words can be used once, more than once or not at all).

brine	electrolysis	hydrogen	lose	Na^+	chlorine atoms
rock salt	sodium hydroxide	Cl^-	chlorine molecule		Cl^- ions
gain	hydrogen molecule	industrial	Cl	chlorine	
chloride	H^+	hydrogen atoms		industrially	

Sodium chloride has many _____ uses. Salt is mined as _____ _____.
This is purified to give sodium chloride. Useful products are obtained from a solution of
sodium chloride called _____ by _____. The ions produced are H^+, OH^-,
_____ and _____. At the anode the _____ ions are deposited. They
_____ electrons and become _____ atoms. Two _____
join together to form a _____ _____. At the cathode the _____ ions are
deposited. They _____ an electron and become _____ atoms. Two
_____ _____ join together to form a _____ _____. All the
products from the electrolysis of brine can be used, as _____ _____ solution is
left in the reaction vessel.

Group 8: The Noble Gases

The Noble Gases think they're above all this reacting business. They're so smug about having a full outer shell, they just sit around all day like they're royalty...

Q1 Here's a few easy ones to start you off...

a) The Noble gases are "inert". **What** does this mean?

b) By referring to their atomic structure, **explain** why the Noble gases are "inert".

c) **Complete** the paragraph below using the word list.
Words can be used once, more than once, or not at all.

Periodic	inert	1%	diatomic	Noble	increase	shell	low	full
helium	individual	argon	neon	electrons	radon	radioactive	8	

The _____ gases are found in Group _____ of the _____ Table.
They are called Noble gases because they do not react with any other element, as they have a _____ outer _____ of _____. They are also called the _____ gases. The Noble gases have very _____ boiling points which _____ down the group. The Noble gas with the largest atoms is _____ and the one with the smallest atoms is _____. Noble gases exist as _____ atoms rather than as _____ molecules. About _____ of the air is made up of Noble gases.

Q2 The table below gives information about the Noble gases. Use it to **answer these questions:**

a) How do the **melting and boiling points** of the gases change as you go down the Group?

b) **Complete** the table by estimating the melting point and boiling point of radon.

Noble Gas	Atomic Number	Density at STP g/cm³	Melting Point °C	Boiling Point °C
Helium	2	0.00017	-272	-269
Neon	10	0.00084	-248	-246
Argon	18	0.0016	-189	-186
Krypton	36	0.0034	-157	-153
Xenon	54	0.006	-112	-108
Radon	86	0.01		

c) **Why** do the **densities** of the Noble gases increase down the group?

Q3 Why is neon used in **advertising signs**?

Neon is Ace!

Q4 Give a **common use** for argon and state why it is used for that purpose.

Q5 Why is helium used in **meteorological balloons**, rather than argon?

Q6 The table below shows some details of the Noble gases.

a) **Fill in the gaps** in the table.

b) **Write down** a noble gas that matches each of these descriptions:

i) Gives out light when a current is passed through it.

ii) Less dense than air.

iii) Used in lasers.

Noble Gas	Symbol	Atomic Number	Mass Number	No. of Protons	No. of Electrons	No. of Neutrons
	He		4	2		
Neon			20	10		
	Ar	18	40			
Krypton			84	36		
Xenon		54	131		54	
Radon		86	222			

Group 1: The Alkali Metals

Q1 The table on the right shows four alkali metals and some of their physical properties.

Alkali Metal	Atomic Mass	Symbol	Boiling Point °C	Melting Point °C	Density g/cm³
Lithium	7		1342	181	0.535
Sodium	23		883	98	0.971
Potassium	39		759	63	0.862
Rubidium	85.5		688	39	1.53

a) Complete the table by filling in their **symbols**.

b) **Explain** why, as you go down Group 1, the atoms get **bigger**.

c) Which element in the table is the **most dense**?

d) Over what **temperature ranges** would you expect **i)** Rubidium, **ii)** Potassium, to be liquids?

Q2 Put the metals in the box in order of reactivity, the most reactive first. Explain why the metals have this order of reactivity.

> Caesium, Potassium, Lithium, Sodium, Rubidium.

Q3 Match up the alkali metal to its reaction in water.

A) Potassium	1) Fizzes vigorously, melts due to the heat given off by the reaction.
B) Sodium	2) Fizzes, giving off hydrogen gas.
C) Lithium	3) Fizzes very vigorously, gives off lots of hydrogen which is ignited by the heat of the reaction. Enough heat is given off to melt the metal.

Q4 Say whether each of these sentences is true or false.

a) Alkali metals form compounds with giant covalent structures.

b) Alkali metal compounds are crystalline and dissolve easily in water.

c) Alkali metals are not very reactive.

d) Alkali metals form ionic compounds.

e) Alkali metals have low density and some will float on water.

Q5 Shown below are two diagrams of atoms.

a) **Complete** the atoms by adding the correct number of electrons for each shell.

b) How can lithium and potassium **achieve** a full outer shell of electrons?

c) What would the **charge** on the ions be?

d) **Write** the **symbol** for each ion formed.

e) In general, the further away the outer electron from the nucleus, the easier it is to remove. Which of lithium and potassium would you expect to be **more reactive**? Explain your answer.

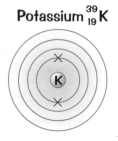

Potassium $^{39}_{19}$K

Lithium $^{7}_{3}$Li

Top Tips: With only <u>one</u> electron in their outer shell, these metals are pretty reactive. The Exam's most likely to ask about <u>trends</u> in the group — make sure you know how <u>size</u>, <u>reactivity</u>, <u>density</u> and <u>melting</u> and <u>boiling points</u> vary down the group... and why.

Reactions of the Alkali Metals

Q1   Group 1 elements of the Periodic Table are known as the **Alkali Metals**. Why is this?

Q2   How are the Alkali metals **stored** and why are they stored this way?

Q3   Alkali metals react with water to produce a gas and a solution.

  a)   What would be the **pH** of the resulting solution?

  b)   Name the **gas** produced. Describe a **test** you could do to confirm your answer.

Q4   Lithium burns in air with a bright red flame.

  a)   Write a **word** equation for the chemical reaction taking place.

  b)   The substance produced in this reaction is added to some dilute sulphuric acid.
Copy and complete the **symbol** equation for this reaction:

$$\text{.................} + H_2SO_4 \rightarrow \text{.................} + Li_2SO_4$$

Q5   **Write out** the **symbol** equations below the picture equations, and **balance** them:

  a)

  b)

  c)

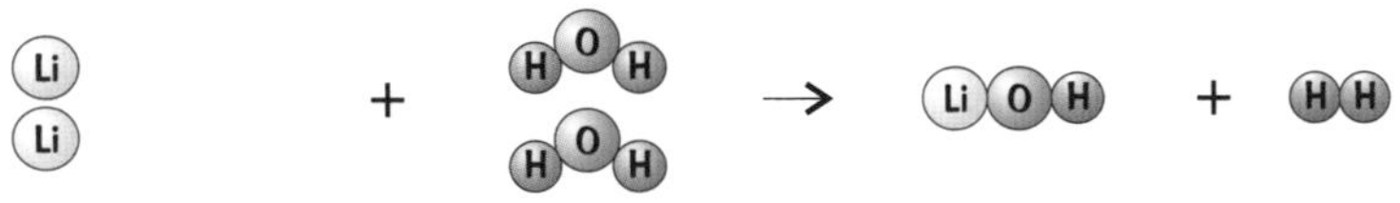

Q6   Rubidium and caesium are very dangerous.

  a)   **Predict** how these react with **water**.

  b)   **Predict** how these react with **air**.

  c)   Why are these two metals so **reactive**?

Q7   When an alkali metal reacts with water, a gas is produced.

  a)   **Complete** the equations to the right.

Sodium + Water →
Lithium + Water →

  b)   **i) Complete** and **balance** this equation: $K_{(s)} + H_2O_{(l)} \rightarrow KOH_{(aq)} +$

    ii) What do the symbols (s), (l), (aq), and (g) stand for in chemical equations?

Group 7: The Halogens

Q1   Why are the halogens known as the Group 7 elements?

Q2   All the halogens form diatomic molecules.

  a)   Explain what is meant by diatomic.

  b)   Write the formula for: **i)** the chlorine molecule.   **ii)** the iodine molecule.

Q3   The halogens also form another type of bond by gaining one electron.

  a)   What is this type of bonding called?

  b)   What would be the charge on a halogen ion?

  c)   Name a compound in which chlorine would gain an electron.

Q4   The reactivity of the halogens decreases down the group, but the reactivity of the alkali metals increases down the group. Explain this difference.

Q5   A lump of potassium reacts with chlorine gas to produce potassium chloride. Write down a balanced symbol equation for this reaction.

Q6   Halogens react violently with alkali metals. Write the word equation for the reaction of each of the halogens below with each of the alkali metals (you should get nine equations in total).

  a)   Chlorine

  b)   Bromine   Lithium   Sodium   Potassium

  c)   Fluorine

Q7   Chlorine is bubbled through sodium bromide as shown in the diagram.

  a)   What would you see happening in the test tube?

  b)   Which of chlorine or bromine is the most reactive?

  c)   Explain why bromine is displaced from the compound by chlorine.

  d)   Complete the equations below:

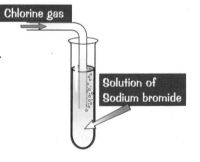

Chlorine gas

Solution of Sodium bromide

            i) Fluorine + Sodium iodide $\rightarrow$

            ii) Chlorine + Sodium bromide $\rightarrow$

            iii) Bromine + Potassium iodide $\rightarrow$

Q8   Give a common use for each of fluorine, chlorine and iodine.

Just hand over the electrons and nobody gets hurt...
Wow, these guys want electrons bad — just one more and they'll have that nice outer-shell feeling...

Transition Metals

Q1 The Transition Metals form a block in the Periodic Table.

Between which two groups in the Periodic table are the transition metals found?

Q2 A metal "X" has a high melting point, can form 2^+ or 3^+ ions, and reacts slowly over a long time with water.

a) **Explain why** you would put this in the transition element block rather than in Group II.

b) This same metal X forms coloured compounds with oxygen.
Write the formula for the combination of this metal with oxygen to form:

  i) X(II) Oxide   **ii)** X(III) Oxide

Q3 **Match** the correct colour to each of these compounds:

1) Copper compound	**A)** Orange / brown
2) Iron(II) compounds	**B)** Blue
3) Iron(III) compounds	**C)** Light green

Q4 Answer these questions on the uses of Transition Metals:

a) **Give a use** for each of these Transition Metals:

  i) Iron   **ii)** Zinc   **iii)** Copper.

b) Why is copper used for household water pipes in **preference** to iron or zinc?

Q5 An element "Y" is a Transition Metal.

a) **Fill in a copy of the table** opposite for the element Y, giving details of its general properties (in terms of good, bad, high, low, etc.).

Conductivity		Density	Malleability	Melting point
Heat	Electricity			

b) Element Y forms 2 ions, Y^+ and Y^{2+}, so it can be used to make a variety of compounds. **Write down** the formulae of the following compounds of the element Y:
  i) Y(I) chloride   **ii)** Y(I) oxide   **iii)** Y(II) oxide

Q6 The transition elements and some of their compounds make good catalysts. **What** is a catalyst?

Q7 Many transition metal carbonates decompose when they are heated.

a) What is the **name** of this type of reaction?

b) Give the **word equation** for the decomposition of $ZnCO_3$.

c) Give the **symbol equation** for the decomposition of $CuCO_3$.

Q8 Sodium hydroxide can be added to solution to test for transition metal ions.

a) Why is this type of reaction called **precipitation**?

b) What would indicate the presence of **iron (II) ions**?

Current, Voltage and Resistance

These questions are about electric current: what it is, what makes it move and what tries to stop it.

Q1 Copy the following paragraph about electric current and **fill the gaps.**

Words to use: electrons, charged, positive, metal, circuit, complete.

A _____ loop is needed for a circuit to work. Current is a flow
of _____ particles around a _____. Electric current can
flow if there are free _____ like in a _____, where
electrons flow throughout the structure of _____ ions.

Q2 **Copy** the circuit diagram and mark on the (+) and (–) on the
cell. **Mark** the direction of the current, ⟶ , and the
direction of the moving electrons, ∙∙∙∙∙∙∙∙∙∙> .

Metal

Q3 **Copy and complete** these sentences using the correct words.

The **current / voltage / resistance** in a circuit flows from **positive / negative** to **positive / negative**.
Electrons flow in the **same direction as / opposite direction to** the flow of "conventional current".

Q4 **Copy the diagram** on the right. **Label** the electrodes
positive (+) and negative (–). **Draw arrows** to show
the movement of ions (⊕⟶▲ , ▲⟵⊖).

Q5 **Copy and complete** the following paragraph about electrolysis.

Use these words:
sodium chloride, sodium chloride solution, liquids, positive, negative, charged particles, dissolved.

Electrolytes are _____ which contain freely moving _____. They are
either ions _____ in water like _____ or molten ionic liquids like
_____. When the current is switched on, the _____ ions move towards
the positive electrode and the _____ ions move towards the negative electrode.

Q6 Electrical wires and connections are made from metal.

Why are metals good conductors of electricity? (Write your answer in terms of **electrons**.)

Current, Voltage and Resistance

Q7   **Draw** a circuit diagram of a 6V battery, a switch and two lamps in series.

Q8   **Draw** a circuit diagram of a 12V power supply with a fuse and a heater in series.

Q9   Complete the table on the right.

Voltage(V)	Current(A)	Resistance(Ω)
230		6.0
230		23.0
6	3.0	
1.5		15.0
12	4.0	
	1.5	5.0

Q10   A kettle is plugged into a 230V mains socket. There is a current of 10A in its element. **Calculate** the resistance of the element.

Q11   Find the current in a resistor of 18 Ω when it is connected to a 9V battery.

Q12   The table below shows measurements of voltage across a component and the current through it.

Voltage(V)	Current(A)
0	0
0.75	1.0
1.50	2.0
2.25	3.0
3.00	4.0
3.75	5.0

a)   **Plot a graph** of voltage (volts) against current (amps).

b)   **Find** the component's resistance.

c)   Is the component a resistor, a filament lamp or a diode?

d)   **Explain** your answer to part **c)** .

Q13   Answer the questions for the circuits **a)** to **f)**.

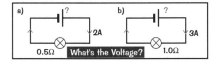 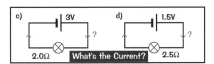 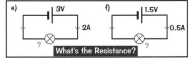

Q14   **Copy and complete** the sentences to describe to describe these situations:

Use these words: lower, slopes, temperature, resistances, increases, one direction, thick.

a)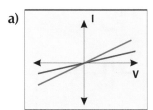

RESISTOR

Different wires have different _____, hence the different _____ on a graph.

b)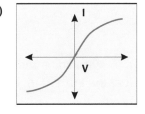

FILAMENT LAMP

As the _____ of the filament _____, the resistance increases.

c)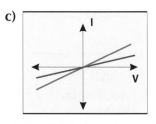

THIN AND THICK WIRE

The graph with the steeper slope is a _____ wire of the same material as it has a _____ resistance.

d)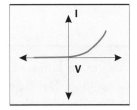

DIODE

Current in a diode can only be in _____ _____.

Circuit Symbols and Devices

Get up to scratch with all this basic electricity stuff — the formulae,
the components and the circuit symbols.

Q1   **Complete the table** for these electrical components. You need to know these for your exam.

CIRCUIT SYMBOL	NAME FOR CIRCUIT SYMBOL	WHAT IT DOES
—⊣⊢—		
	LDR	
		Converts electrical energy into sound energy.
—Ⓥ—		
		Wire inside it breaks if the current is too high, protecting the appliance.
—▭—		
	Thermistor	
	Open Switch	
		Allows current in one direction only.
		Adjusted to alter the current in a circuit.
—Ⓜ—		
	Ammeter	

Q2   Match the words with their correct description on the right.

a) current

b) resistance

c) diode

d) watt (W)

e) electrolyte

f) amp (A)

g) ammeter

h) voltmeter

i) copper

j) volt (V)

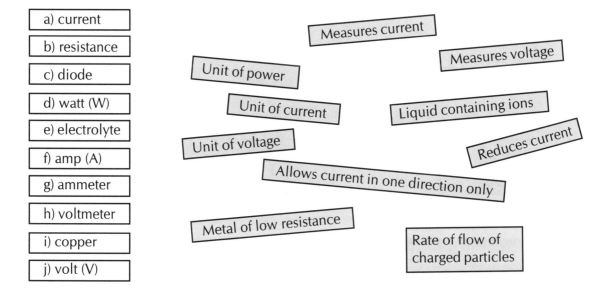

Measures current

Measures voltage

Unit of power

Unit of current

Liquid containing ions

Unit of voltage

Reduces current

Allows current in one direction only

Metal of low resistance

Rate of flow of charged particles

Q3   **Redraw** this circuit with an ammeter and a voltmeter correctly
placed to measure the current in, and voltage across the motor M.

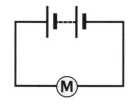

Top Tips: You've got to know all of these basics about electricity before you move on —
sure it's not particularly exciting, but that's just the way the cookie crumbles. You'll definitely need to
know those symbols at the top and the basic definitions, so make sure that you do...

Circuit Symbols and Devices

Q4 Use the data in the table opposite to plot a graph of resistance, R, against light intensity. **Draw** the best fit curve.

Resistance(Ω)	Light Intensity (units)
9200	0.2
7100	0.5
5500	1.0
3600	2.0
2500	3.0
1200	5.0
400	8.0
200	10.0

a) How does the resistance change as the light gets brighter?

b) How does the resistance change as the light gets dimmer?

c) How does the **slope** of the graph change as the light gets brighter — and what does this say about the change in resistance?

d) Give **two uses** for light dependent resistors and **explain** how one of them works (drawing the circuit diagram may help).

Q5 The graph below shows how the resistance of a thermistor changes with temperature.

a) Briefly **describe** what happens to the resistance of the thermistor as the temperature changes.

b) What is the resistance at 25°C (approximately)?

c) Give an example of a thermistor in use.

d) What **change in temperature** increases the resistance from 90 Ω to 130 Ω?

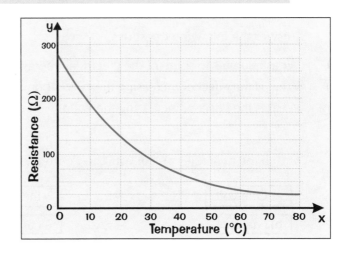

Q6 Electrical current can be supplied by batteries and by mains electricity.

a) What type of current do **batteries** supply?

b) What about **mains** electricity?

c) What is the difference between **AC** and **DC** in terms of current flow?

d) **Cathode ray oscilloscopes** (CRO) can be used to distinguish between AC and DC flow. What types of current are displayed by the CROs on the right?

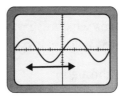 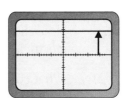

Top Tips: AC DC but no music I'm afraid. Still this is easy enough to learn as long as you make the effort to go over the questions carefully, and check your answers afterwards. Light dependent resistors and thermistors have features that you just need to remember for easy marks.

Energy Change

Q1 **Complete** the two tables below.

a)

What it is?	Letter	Unit	Symbol
Voltage	V	volts	V
Current	I		
		ohms	Ω
	E	joules	
Electrical Charge	Q		
	t	seconds	
Power		watts	

b)

If a current of:	flows for:	-then the charge passing is
1 ampere	1 second	1 coulomb
2 amperes	1 second	2 coulomb
2 amperes	2 seconds	
4 amperes	3 seconds	
5 amperes		15 coulombs
	5 seconds	30 coulombs
10 amperes	6 seconds	

Q2 Answer these questions about **charge** and **energy**.

a) Find the energy supplied by a torch battery, voltage 6V, if 1500C of charge flows.

b) Find the energy supplied by four 3V radio batteries if 250C of charge flows.

c) Find the energy supplied to a camera by a 1.5V lithium battery if 6C of charge flows.

Q3 Answer the following questions.

a) **What happens** to some of the electrical energy when current flows through a **resistor**?

b) What is the effect of increasing the **current** on the amount of heat energy produced?

c) What is the effect of increasing the **voltage** on the amount of heat energy produced?

Q4 **Match** the quantities **a) – e)** with their correct description on the right:

a) One volt — is the energy transferred per unit of charge passed

b) Energy — is current × time

c) One ampere — is one coulomb every second

d) Voltage — is one joule per coulomb

e) Charge — is charge × voltage

Q5 Household appliances which use mains electricity are labelled with their **power rating**.

a) What current flows through:

i) A fan of 60 W.

ii) A kettle of power rating 2750 W.

iii) A microwave rated at 800 W.

iv) A 1500 W toaster.

Use mains electricity = 230 V.

b) What is the power rating of a radio (running off the mains) which has 0.2 A flowing through it?

Energy Change

Q6   A dimmer switch controls the brightness of a light: turn it clockwise to increase the brightness, or anti-clockwise to decrease it. It works by using a variable resistor to control the current in the bulb.

It is illustrated in the diagram opposite.

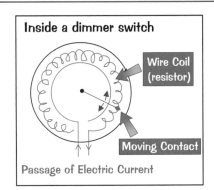

Inside a dimmer switch

Wire Coil (resistor)

Moving Contact

Passage of Electric Current

a)   Draw the path followed by the current if the lights are **dim**; **medium brightness**; and **bright**.

Below are three readings of current and resistance taken from the switch at different settings.

b)   Complete the table using the same descriptions for brightness used in part **a)**.

c)   What happens to the size of the current when the resistance is increased?

d)   What happens to the size of the current when the resistance is decreased?

Brightness of Lights	Current(A)	Resistance(Ω)
	1.0	6.0
	2.0	3.0
	3.0	2.0

Q7   **Find** the missing values of energy, charge and voltage in the table below.

Energy (J)	Charge (C)	Voltage (V)
500	50	
	15	3
4800		240
10 000		20
	75	12

Q8   This diagram shows a water heating experiment.

The experiment is started. After a certain time, the water temperature is measured. How will the temperature compare if we:

a)   increase the voltage to 24V?

b)   replace the heating coil with one of half the resistance?

c)   replace the coil with a shorter one of the same total resistance?

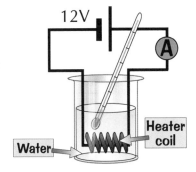

12V

A

Water

Heater coil

Q9   Answer these **multiple choice** questions about **energy, power** and **resistance.**

a)   If a voltage in a circuit is changed from 6V to 12V, how much more energy will be picked up by each charge passing through the circuit?

A. Three times as much   **B.** Twice as much   **C.** Six times as much

b)   Each coulomb carries 12J of energy. If the current flowing in the circuit is 3A, what is the total power supplied?

A. 3W   **B.** 4W   **C.** 36W

c)   What is the total resistance of the circuit?

A. 3Ω   **B.** 4Ω   **C.** 12Ω

Static Electricity

Charges don't just flow around circuits. They're everywhere,
getting ready to build up and zap you when you're least expecting it.

Q1   Match up words **a) – k)** with appropriate sentence endings from the list.

a)	Positive (+) and negative (–) charges	— is caused by friction.
b)	Static electricity	— repel each other.
c)	Only negative (–) charges	— by connecting it to earth.
d)	Voltage	— the greater the voltage.
e)	Induced charge	— repel each other.
f)	The greater the charge	— are attracted to each other.
g)	You can discharge a conductor	— builds up if charge builds up.
h)	Two negative (–) charges	— is lost if the charged rod is moved away.
i)	A rod will be negatively (–) charged	— move, never the positive charges.
j)	Two positive (+) charges	— if electrons are rubbed off.
k)	A rod will be positively (+) charged	— if electrons are rubbed on.

Q2   The diagram shows a duster and a polythene rod, both insulating materials. Copy the diagram.

a) Use arrows to show the movement of charge when the rod is rubbed with a duster.

b) Show the type of charge left on each object.

c) What happens to small pieces of paper or cork which are placed next to a charged rod?

Q3   Static electricity can cause visible sparks to fly. **Copy and complete** this paragraph by choosing the correct word from each pair in bold.

> As the charge on an isolated object **increases / decreases**, the **voltage / distance** between the object and earth increases. If this voltage is **small / high** enough and an **earthed / isolated** conductor is brought near the object, a **spark / small flea** may jump across the gap between them.

Q4   The movement of electrons (earthing) removes the excessive charge from materials.

a) Explain why you can get a shock by touching your car door after driving.

b) How does walking on carpet produce a static charge?
What happens if you touch a metal pipe after walking on carpet?

Q5   Why do you sometimes get a shock from your synthetic jumper when you take it off?
Use these terms in your answer: 'static charges', 'movement of electrons', 'sparks/shocks'.

Q6   Static electricity can be lethal.

a) List **three** working situations where static can lead to dangerous sparks in the workplace.

b) Choose one situation you listed in **a)**.
Draw a diagram to show how the static builds up. **Label** the (+) and (–) charges.

c) For your example in **b)**, **explain** the solution to the problem.

Q7   **Draw a diagram** to show how lightning occurs. Include on your diagram: the cloud, raindrops, Earth, and positive and negative charges.

Module PD4 — Using Electricity

Static Electricity — Examples

You've probably used static electricity without realising it —
it doesn't always give itself away by shocking you.

Q1 Static electricity can be really useful. Give **three practical uses** of static electricity.

Q2 This diagram shows how an inkjet printer works. Fill in the gaps to explain what's happening at the places labelled ① to ④.

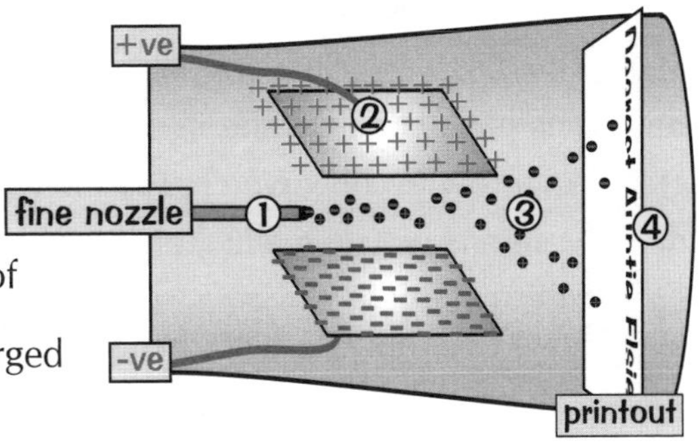

① Ink is forced out of the ....
It's very .... so that the ink droplets
become ....

② A .... is applied across two plates made of
.... One plate will be .... charged
while the other will be .... charged.

③ The ink droplets pass between the plates. The droplets are ....
to the plate with the .... charge and .... from the plate
with the .... charge. This spreading-out is called ....

④ The .... across the plates is .... so that each droplet is
.... to a different place on the paper. Each drop is so ....
that it takes many of them to make up just one letter on your print-out.

labels on diagram: +ve, ②, fine nozzle ①, ③, ④, -ve, printout

Q3 Static electricity is used to attract black toner to paper in a **photocopier**. Put these sentences in the right order.

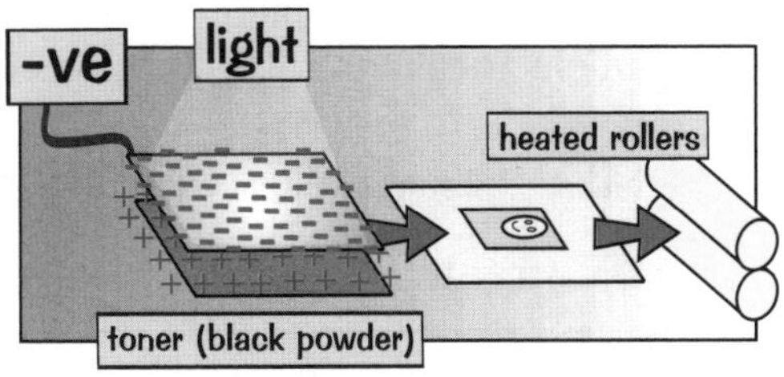

diagram labels: -ve, light, heated rollers, toner (black powder)

A The toner is transferred to the paper.

G Perfect black and white copy emerges from copier.

C Calendar is placed on the glass and 'copy' button pressed.

E The toner sticks to the paper.

I The paper is heated in the rollers.

B Image of Mr March is projected onto the plate.

D The toner is attracted to the charged bits of the plate.

F Katy needs a copy of Mr March from her 'Tasty Firemen' Calendar.

H Copying plate is charged electronically.

J Electric charge leaks away from areas of the plate with more light falling on them.

Top Tips: Next time you take a photocopy you'll know exactly what's going on. Great. Still it's good to know that all of this physics info is actually useful in the real world. It's probably going to be useful to you in the Exam as well, so learn these uses of static electricity well...

Electric Motors

A wire carrying current will produce a magnetic field, and a moving magnet can produce electricity.
Hmmmm... just remember the rules of Sir John Ambrose Fleming and you'll be fine.

Q1   **Draw** a diagram to represent Fleming's Left Hand Rule. Label it fully.

Q2   **Copy** the diagram below showing two magnets with a current-carrying wire between them.
Draw on the diagram:

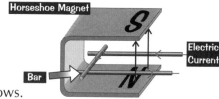

a)   The direction of the current.

b)   The magnetic field and its direction.

c)   An arrow to show which way the wire will move.

d)   State one way to make the wire move in the opposite direction.

e)   State **two** things you could do to increase the size of the force on the wire.

f)   If the wire was turned through 90° so that it ran along the magnetic field, would there still be a force? **Explain** your answer.

Q3   The diagram opposite shows a horseshoe magnet. There is an electric current in a wire between the poles. A metal bar completes the circuit and rests freely on the wires.

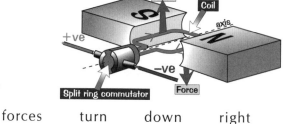

Describe the **motion** of the bar when a **direct current** flows.
Describe the **motion** of the bar when an **alternating current** flows.

Q4   The diagram shows how a simple motor works. The coil is free to rotate between the poles of the magnet. The split ring commutator makes an electrical contact with the coil.

Fill in the gaps below using the **following words**:

current   up   torque   coil   forces   turn   down   right

> When there is a current in the _____ , the left side is pushed _____ and the _____ side _____. When the coil is vertical, the forces can't _____ it any further because there is no _____ . As the coil passes the vertical, the split ring commutator changes the direction of the _____ within the coil. This means the _____ on the coil continue to push it in the direction it is already turning.

Q5   **Link up** each description **a)** to **f)** with the correct word from the right-hand column.

a) Swaps the contacts every half turn in an electric motor	• coil (armature)
b) Keep a good electrical contact with the commutator	• polarity
c) Converts electrical energy into kinetic energy	• electric motor
d) Turns around on an axis	• carbon brushes
e) Positive and negative	• split ring commutator

Electromagnetic Induction

Q1 A model train travels at high speed into a tunnel. A bar magnet is fixed to
the top of the train. A coil of insulated wire is wound around the tunnel
and underneath the track. A buzzer completes the circuit formed by the coil.

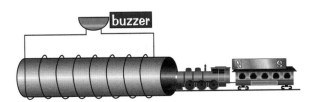

   a) **Explain** why the buzzer sounds when the train
passes through the tunnel.

   b) Would the buzzer sound if the train stopped in
the tunnel? **Explain** your answer.

   c) Suggest **two** ways to make the buzzer sound
louder (without dismantling the tunnel and coil).

Q2 A magnet is being pushed towards a coil of insulated wire.

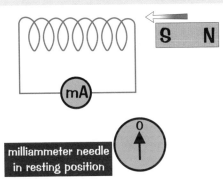

Magnet pushed in	Needle moved to the right
Magnet in the coil - not moving	
Magnet pulled out	
Magnet pulled out faster	

   a) The table above summarises four experiments with the magnet. Copy and complete the table.

   b) Which **type** of pole (N or S) is produced at the ends of the coil when the magnet is pushed in?
Explain your answer.

   c) Suggest **two** ways to reverse the poles produced in the coil.

Q3 A wire is moved upwards through a magnetic field, as shown in the diagram below.

   a) A current is induced in the wire.
What is the effect of:

   i) using a **stronger** magnet.

   ii) moving the wire **faster**.

   iii) moving the wire towards one of the **poles**.

   b) What's the name for the effect of moving a wire and a magnetic field relative to each other?

Q4 Below is data about a small lab generator, a generator in a power station, and a dynamo.

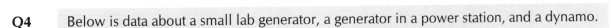

a) Uses a permanent magnet which rotates.

b) Generates a current of 20,000A
   at a voltage of 25,000V.

c) Generates a current less than 1A.

d) Uses a stationary permanent magnet.

e) Produces alternating current, AC.

f) Produces direct current, DC.

g) Has a magnet spinning at 50 times a second.

h) Has a magnet spinning at variable speeds.

Draw a table with the columns: **lab generator**, **power station generator** and **dynamo**.
Write out the data in the correct column. You can use the data once, more than once or not at all.

Electromagnetic Induction

Q5   **Re-order** the words to reveal the **four factors** that affect the size of the induced voltage.

| the coil | The strength of | the magnet | of turns | The number |
| The speed of | The area of | the movement | | on the coil |

Q6   Use these words to **fill in** the gaps.
      swap   slip   motor   voltage   rotate
      higher   more   voltage   faster   magnetic

Generators _____ a coil in a _____ field. Their construction is quite like a _____ ,
except there are _____ rings instead of a split ring commutator, so the contacts don't
_____ every half turn. This means they produce alternating _____ . _____
revolutions produce not only _____ peaks, but _____ overall _____ too.

Q7   Below is a cathode ray oscilloscope (CRO) display for a generator. **Draw in the trace** to show how
the current from a generator changes as the coil rotates. Then **fill in** the blanks in the sentences.

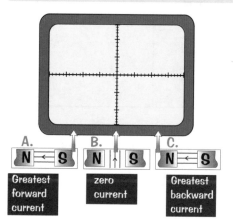

Use these words once each:
field cuts horizontal vertical zero greatest rapidly

a) The current is _____ when the coil is
_____ . The coil _____ magnetic
field lines most _____ in this position.

b) The current is _____ when the coil is
_____ . The coil does not cut
_____ lines in this position.

c) Once again, the current is greatest when the
coil is horizontal.

Q8   There are two **step-up** and two **step-down** transformers here. Which are which?

(The primary coil is on
the left and the
secondary on the right).

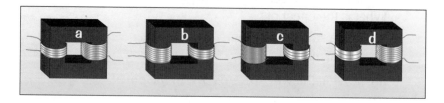

Q9   This table shows the number of turns on the
above transformers, and the input voltage.
Find the **output voltage** in each case.

Transformer	a	b	c	d
Input turns	5	8	16	3
Output turns	10	4	4	9
Input voltage	230	230	24	24
Output voltage				

Q10   **Explain** the following terms used to describe transformers.

a) Magnetic field   **c)** Electromagnetic induction   **e)** Ratio

b) Primary coil   **d)** Secondary coil

Q11   **Explain why** you can't get transformers to work with DC (direct current).

The National Grid

Q1   The **rate** of energy transfer (**power**) is given by the equation below:

| Power loss due to heat generated (P) | = | Potential Difference (V) | × | Current (I) |

The **National Grid** contains power lines that carry electricity at 120,000 volts.

a)   Rewrite the above equation in terms of **I** (current) and **R** (resistance).

b)   If a current twice as big as before is used with the same voltage, what will happen to the power loss?

c)   Using your new equation can you suggest why electricity is carried at such a high voltage on the National Grid?

d)   Calculate the number of turns in a **primary coil** needed to step down from a National Grid power line to a **secondary coil** of 100 turns connected to a normal 230V domestic supply.

e)   In most factories, machines use a 110V power supply.

Calculate the number of turns in a **primary coil** required to step down from a 230V supply to a **secondary coil** of 2000 turns connected to a 110V machine.

Q2   The diagram below shows a typical arrangement of a generator.

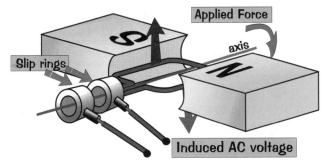

a)   What is the purpose of the slip rings and brushes?

b)   What happens as the coil is rotated?

c)   Complete the following sentences by choosing the correct words from the brackets.

   i) The induced voltage (**increases** / **decreases**) as the speed of movement decreases.

   ii) The induced voltage increases as the strength of the magnetic field is (**increased** / **decreased**).

   iii) The induced voltage (**increases** / **decreases**) as the area of the coil is (**increased** / **decreased**).

Mary had a little lamb — she tied it to a pylon...

You need to learn the generator diagram with all the parts and the transformer equation — everything's easy after that. You can calculate those 'step ups' and 'step downs' to your heart's content.

The National Grid

Q3 The diagram below shows how electricity is generated and sent to homes and industry.

a) **Add labels** onto the diagram to show the process involved in the National Grid.

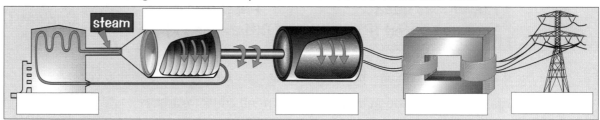

b) **Complete** the following using each of these words once:

induction   oil   uranium fuel   steam   gas   coal   turbine   generator   magnetic

Heat energy in a power station is produced by burning fossil fuels such as _____ ,
_____ or _____ . _____ _____ is used in nuclear power stations.
The boiler makes _____ which drives a _____ , which turns a _____ .
The generator produces electricity using the principle of electromagnetic _____ .
This happens when a metal coil is rotated in a strong _____ field .

Q4 **Match** these pairs of statements about the National Grid and Mains Electricity.

a) Cables are at a high voltage	due to resistance of the cables.
b) Power supplied	requires transformers as well as big pylons with huge insulators.
c) To transmit a lot of power	equals I² × R.
d) A high current means a loss of energy as heat	for efficient transmission.
e) Power loss due to resistance in the cables	is best calculated using V × I.
f) It's cheaper to boost the voltage up to 400,000V	to keep the current low.
g) Boosting the voltage up to 400,000V	you need a high voltage or a high current.
h) Transformers step-up voltage	and keep the current very low.
i) Transformers step-down voltage to our homes	because transformers don't work with DC.
j) Voltage has to be AC on the National Grid	to bring it back to safe, useable levels.

Q5 Letter Check! Are you getting confused by all these letters? **Write down** what each one stands for.

a) Symbols for quantities: **i)** V **ii)** I **iii)** P **iv)** R
b) Letters for units: **i)** Ω **ii)** A **iii)** W **iv)** V

Q6 Pair up the units in question 3 with the quantities they represent.

Q7 **Pair up the words...** ⟹ ...and meanings below:

a) Transmit	motor driven by steam
b) AC	place for generating and distributing electrical power
c) DC	direct current
d) Turbine	send from one place to another
e) Power station	changes the voltage of an alternating current supply
f) Transformer	alternating current

Module PD5 — Applications of Physics

Work Done and Power

Work done is an easy idea to get your head around.
And power is just the work you do each second. No probs.

Q1 The table shows the force exerted by a sprinter with different types of training shoe. It also shows the distance moved by the sprinter in a short time.

a) State the formula connecting work done, force and distance.

Copy the table and complete the final column showing the work done.

b) What units should be used for the work done column?

c) What forces are the work done against?

The sprinter decides to test the Two Stripes shoe further by going for a run. For 15 seconds of this time, she runs at a constant velocity of 9m/s.

Brand of trainer	Force (N)	Distance (m)	Work Done
Two Stripes	4.2	1.6	
Big Cross	5.6	0.8	
Off Balance	4.8	1.2	
Obverse	5.9	1.4	
High Vest	4.5	0.9	

d) Calculate the **work done** and **power** developed during those 15s.

Q2 My old car's broken down — luckily the road is flat. There is a garage 1500 metres away. The car manual says it needs a minimum force of 700N to push the car along a flat road.

a) What is the **minimum energy** needed to push the car to the garage?

The car goes over a broken bottle, still 600m from the garage.
A tyre bursts and the force of friction increases the required pushing force to 900N.

b) Calculate the **total energy consumption** in this case.

Someone mentions that there is another garage only 1300m away from where my car broke down, but the last 100m are uphill, and the pushing force here would have had to be 1150N.

c) Would I have saved any energy by pushing the car to this garage, assuming that in both cases I had avoided any broken bottles?

Q3 Scott and Sheila are water-skiing over a 400m course. When it's Scott's turn, a forcemeter on the tow rope registers a force of 475N. When Sheila has a go, the forcemeter registers 425N.

a) Calculate the **energy** needed to pull each skier over the course.

b) Why would the **total energy** consumed by the boat be **more** than this in each case?

Scott now starts to show off by giving piggyback rides to passing sharks. He does this 4 times, each for 30m. For the remainder of the 400m course, he is by himself. During each piggyback, the forcemeter measures 720N.

c) Calculate the **energy** needed to pull Scott and his fishy friends over the course in this case.

d) If the average power output from the boat is 2kW, how long does it take for them to complete the course (to the nearest second)?

Like the tortoise, slow and steady wins the race...

Make sure to remember work done = force x distance. If you get a two-part question, just make sure you're careful to add up the right bits to get the total work done. Learn that and you're sorted.

Kinetic Energy and Potential Energy

For these questions take g, the acceleration due to gravity, as 10m/s².

Q1   Answer these questions on the basics of **kinetic energy**.

a)   What is the **formula** for kinetic energy?

b)   What do each of the terms in the equation **stand for**?

c)   Give three examples of the **kinds** of objects that have kinetic energy.

Q2   Some questions on **gravitational potential energy**.

a)   What is the **formula** for gravitational potential energy?

b)   What do each of the terms **stand for**?

c)   What **kinds** of objects gain or lose gravitational potential energy?

Q3   The table below consists of a list of statements. **Write down** which are true, and which are false.

a) If two objects have the same velocity, the one with the **greater mass** will have **more kinetic energy**.
b) Two objects of the **same mass** will always have the **same kinetic energy**.
c) If one object is **twice as high** above a particular point of the surface of the Earth as another with the same mass, it will have **twice the kinetic energy**.
d) **Kinetic energy** is measured in **Joules**.
e) The **faster** an object travels, the greater its **potential energy**.
f) The gravitational field strength, g, is important when working out **kinetic energy**.
g) Two cans of different mass on the **same shelf** have the **same gravitational potential energy**.

Q4   The table below gives some figures about velocity and kinetic energy for a car that is standing at traffic lights, and begins to accelerate away (at time t = 0) once they have turned green.

Time (s)	Velocity (m/s)	Kinetic Energy (J)
0.0	0	
0.5	10	
1.0	30	
1.5		2,662,875

The mass of the car is 2630kg. **Copy** and **complete** the table.

Q5   Which of the following has the most **kinetic energy**?

a) A cricket ball, mass 0.4kg travelling at 40m/s.	**b)** An athlete of mass 70kg jogging at 5m/s.
c) A cocker spaniel of mass 15kg running at 10m/s.	**d)** A robot of mass 1000kg moving at 0.6m/s.
e) A bullet of mass 0.005kg travelling at 250m/s.	

Q6   A light aircraft is taking a group of parachutists up into the air. Dressed in her parachuting gear, Amy has a mass of 90kg. The aircraft takes the group up to a height of 5000m before they jump.

a)   How much **gravitational potential energy** does Amy gain?

Amy jumps from the aircraft and falls to a height of 3000m before opening her main parachute.

b)   How much more gravitational potential energy does she have at this point than when she was on the ground?

The main parachute fails to open properly. Amy jettisons it — its mass is 5kg — and opens her reserve parachute.

c)   How much gravitational potential energy does she have when she is 1500m above the ground?

Kinetic Energy and Potential Energy

Q7 A tourist's Fiat is driving along a mountain road. The combined mass of the car and luggage is 2920kg. The car is powering uphill at 23m/s.

a) **How much** kinetic energy does the car have at this point?

At the top of the road, the car has gained a total height of 1200m.

b) **Calculate** the potential energy gained by the car.

As the car rounds a bend at the top of the mountain, a suitcase falls from the roof into the valley below. The suitcase has a mass of 20kg.

c) Work out the **potential energy** the suitcase has lost after falling a distance of 60m.

d) If all of the potential energy of the suitcase is converted into kinetic energy, **how fast** will it be travelling when it has fallen 60m?

e) Explain why **in reality** it will not actually be travelling as fast as this.

Q8 Some workmen are using a rope to lower a bucket full of bricks from a window. They tie off the rope when the bucket is just above the ground. As they are making their way downstairs to unload the bricks, a strong wind sets the bucket swinging.

Draw a diagram of the **path** of the swinging bucket. On your diagram:

    mark with the letter A — where the **potential** energy is greatest.

    mark with the letter B — where the **kinetic** energy is greatest.

    mark with the letter C — where the bucket is travelling **fastest**.

    mark with the letter D — where the bucket's **velocity** is zero.

Q9 A bouncy ball has a mass of 0.3kg. It is dropped from a height of 3 m.

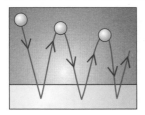

a) **How much** potential energy has the ball lost when it hits the ground?

b) Ignoring air resistance, **how fast** will the ball be travelling?
The ball rebounds vertically at a speed of 7.0m/s.

c) What **kinetic energy** does it now have?

d) What **height** will it reach on the rebound?

e) **Explain** what has happened to the energy that the ball has lost.

f) What is the **percentage efficiency** of the bounce?

Q10 Three students carry out an experiment to compare their own personal power. They measure their weight, then time how long it takes them to run up a flight of stairs 12m high. Their results are shown in the table below. **Copy and complete** the table.

Name	Weight (N)	Time (s)	Potential Energy Gained (J)	Power (W)
Alex	520	14		
Billie	450	16		
Jack	600	15		

Digital and Analogue Signals

Q1   Information such as speech or music can be converted into electrical signals.

a)   What are the **two** ways of transmitting this information?

b)   Write down the ways in which they are **different**.

c)   **List three** examples of devices which use each type of signal.

Q2   Decide whether the following statements are **true or false**. If false, write out the correct version.

a)   The **amplitude** and **frequency** of **digital** signals vary continuously.

b)   **Digital** pulses can take one of only **two** values.

c)   Clocks and dimmer switches can **both** be **analogue** devices.

d)   Clocks and on/off switches can **both** be **digital** devices.

e)   The problem with **digital** signals is that they lose quality relatively quickly.

f)   **Digital** signals are capable of transmitting far more information than analogue ones (within a given time).

Q3   Signals often need to be **amplified** along their route or at their destination.

a)   Why is this necessary?

b)   What else usually happens to a signal between its source and its destination? (**Hint:** it picks up something unwanted).

c)   In what ways do analogue and digital signals differ in their response to amplification?

Q4   Rearrange these pictures into **two sets of seven** (including arrows) to show:

a)   Analogue signals picking up noise and then being amplified.

b)   Digital signals picking up noise and then being amplified.

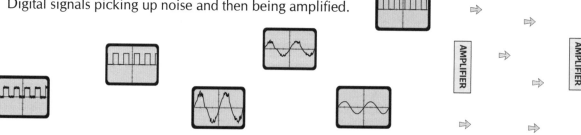

Q5   It is possible to change a digital signal to an analogue one and vice versa.

a)   What are the names of the two devices used to do this?

b)   Give an example of something that contains both of them.

Pulsating stuff this...

This is all very practical, so you can bet you'll get a question on it.
Make sure you know the _differences_ between analogue and digital signals, and _why_ digital signals are better.
And "because we can watch the footy and loads of cool movies" is not an Exam answer.

EM Waves for Communication

Q1   Copy and complete these sentences about electromagnetic waves.

Use these words: **radio   light   refracted   same speed   infra-red
microwaves   diffracted   reflected**

a)   All electromagnetic waves travel at the _____ _____ in a vacuum.

b)   _____, _____, _____ and _____ can carry information.

c)   Like light, all radiation used for communication can be _____, _____ and _____.

Q2   A **special property** of light is shown in the diagrams below. Complete these sentences about it.

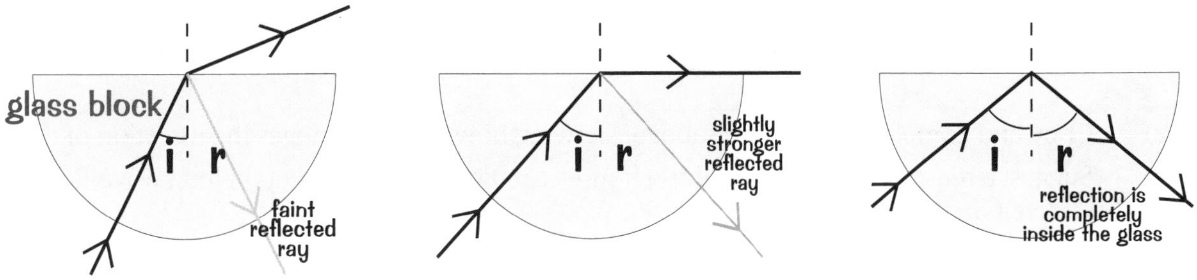

glass block

faint reflected ray

slightly stronger reflected ray

reflection is completely inside the glass

a)   When light attempts to exit a **dense** medium (eg. glass), at an angle to the normal
greater than the _____ _____, **all** of the light is reflected inside the medium.

b)   This phenomenon is called _____ _____ _____.
It has important practical uses, for example in _____ fibres.

c)   Optical communications have several advantages over **electrical signals** in wires.
Fill in the blanks to say what they are.

i) The signal doesn't need to be _____ as often.
ii) A cable of the same diameter can carry a lot more _____.
iii) In theory, **no information** whatsoever would be **lost** at each _____.
However some light is lost due to **surface imperfections**, so the signal still needs
_____ every few km.

d)   In **medicine**, an _____, which consists of a narrow bunch of optical fibres,
is used to view the inside of the body.

Q3   Decide whether each of the statements **a)** to **j)** below are **true or false.**
If **false**, write down what the **highlighted words** should be replaced with.

a)   **Microwaves** are used to communicate with satellites.
b)   **Microwaves** are the same thing as heat radiation.
c)   **Gamma rays** can both cause and cure cancer.
d)   **Only visible light** can be diffracted.
e)   **Radio waves** can have wavelengths of many metres.
f)   **X-rays** are used to take pictures of bones because they are relatively safe.
g)   **Infrared** radiation causes skin cancer.
h)   **Microwaves** are absorbed by water.
i)   **Long wave radiowaves** are able to diffract long distances round the Earth.
j)   **Visible light** has a wavelength of about a ten thousandth of a millimetre.

The electromagnetic ray
loved tinned food. It
really stuck on him.

EM Waves for Communication

Q4 The diagrams below show short wave TV waves and long wave radio waves approaching a hill.

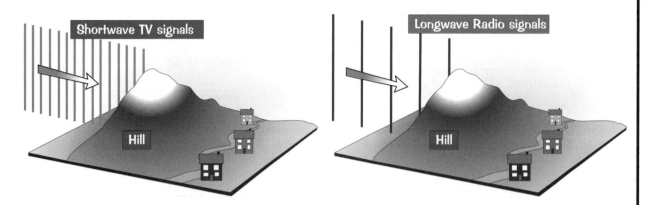

a) Copy and complete the pictures above, showing how the hill changes the direction of the EM wave.

b) Suggest a reason why people in these houses can **listen** to the cricket on long wave Radio 5 but not **watch** it on the television.

Q5 **Label** this diagram of satellite transmission and **fill in** the gaps below.

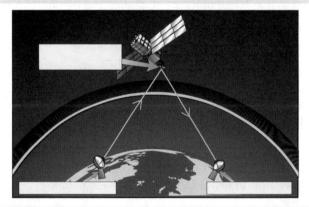

The microwave signal is transmitted _____ into space by a _____ _____ _____ dish in one part of the world. The signal is picked up by the _____ _____ _____ orbiting thousands of km above the Earth. The satellite _____ the signal back to Earth in a different _____ where it's then received by another _____ dish in another part of the _____.

Q6 Long-distance communication can be achieved in two different ways. One way is via satellite, the other is by reflecting waves.

What part of the Earth's atmosphere are the waves reflected off?

Q7 Refraction and diffraction of radiation can affect satellite communications.

a) Where does refraction occur?

b) What property of the microwaves makes this happen?

c) Where does the diffraction occur?

Basic Mechanics

Q1 The Broughton Space Agency (BSA) are testing two new **rocket** designs for an important mission.

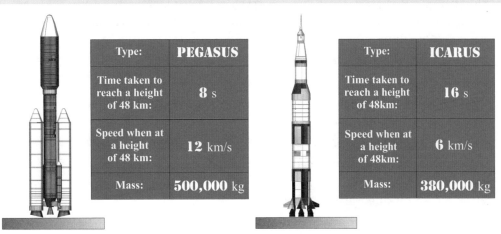

Type:	**PEGASUS**
Time taken to reach a height of 48 km:	**8** s
Speed when at a height of 48 km:	**12** km/s
Mass:	**500,000** kg

Type:	**ICARUS**
Time taken to reach a height of 48km:	**16** s
Speed when at a height of 48km:	**6** km/s
Mass:	**380,000** kg

a) Calculate in m/s² the average **acceleration** of each rocket between the ground and a height of 48km.

b) Assuming that its mass doesn't change, what is the overall **force** needed to provide Icarus' acceleration?

c) What is the size of the **gravitational force** acting on Pegasus? What is another name for this force?

d) Pegasus travels at a **speed** of 12 km/s when at an altitude of 48 km. What other piece of information would you need to give in order to specify its **velocity**?

e) Once it has passed this altitude, Pegasus moves with a **constant** velocity. What does this tell you about the **forces** acting on it?

f) Unfortunately, the scientists working on Icarus have got their calculations wrong. After a short while its engines fail and it begins to **free–fall** towards the ground. What can you say about its acceleration now?

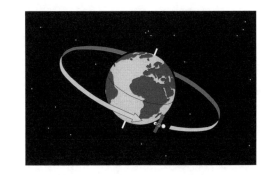

Q2 Pegasus is chosen for the mission. The mission is a success and a new communications satellite is put into **orbit** above the Earth.

Answer the following questions:

a) The satellite has a **circular** orbit and travels at a constant speed. Is its velocity constant? Explain your answer.

b) Is the satellite **accelerating**? Explain your answer.

c) What is the name of the **force** required for circular motion?

d) What provides this force in the case of the satellite?

Q3 The next BSA mission involves sending a shuttle to a space station.

Once the shuttle has been launched into space, it fires its thrusters and **accelerates** to the station.

Explain in terms of forces, how it is possible for the shuttle to accelerate in space, even though there is no **air** for it to push off against.

Basic Mechanics

Q4   Answer **true** or **false**.

a)   A feather and a hamster will not land at the same time if dropped from the same height above the Moon.

b)   Acceleration equals force times mass.

c)   The drag force depends on shape and area.

d)   The forces of air resistance and weight are equal when a falling object is travelling at its maximum speed (terminal velocity).

e)   The speed at which weight equals air resistance is the same whether a falling sky diver has his/her parachute open or not.

Q5   **Fill** in the gaps using the given words.

same   weight   drag   resistance   falling

The downward force acting on all _____ objects is gravity, which would make them fall at the _____ rate if it wasn't for air _____ . The terminal velocity of any object is determined by its _____ in comparison to the _____ of it.

Q6   **Plot the graph** of velocity (in m/s) [vertical axis] against time (in s) [horizontal axis] showing the motion of a human skydiver after jumping out of an aeroplane. Then answer these questions:

a)   **Find** the terminal velocity of the skydiver (be sure to give the units).

b)   **Estimate** the velocity of the skydiver after:

      i) 5s   **ii)** 12.5s.

c)   At what time does the skydiver reach terminal velocity?

d)   The skydiver opens her parachute 20 seconds after jumping out of the aeroplane. Describe the extra force acting on her and its effect upon her speed.

e)   Will the skydiver reach a new terminal velocity? **Explain** your answer.

Velocity (m/s)	Time (s)
0	0
4.5	2
16.5	4
23.0	6
29.0	8
36.0	10
43.5	12
50.0	14
56.0	16
60.0	18
60.0	20

Q7   **Draw** the diagrams below showing the resultant forces. If the body is accelerating, write down the direction (up, down, right or left) in which it is accelerating.

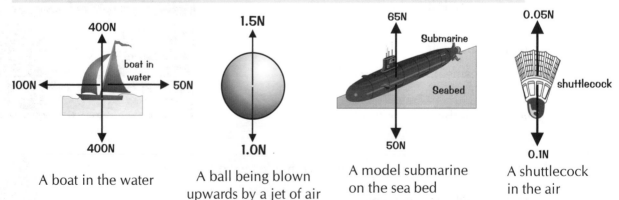

A boat in the water   A ball being blown upwards by a jet of air   A model submarine on the sea bed   A shuttlecock in the air

Top Tips

The idea of <u>resultant force</u> is really important. The resultant force is just the <u>overall force</u> acting on an object. You get it by adding or subtracting forces that act in the same direction. Obviously, it's the overall resultant force that decides if the object <u>accelerates</u>, <u>decelerates</u> or stays at a <u>steady speed</u>.

The Planets

Q1 This question consists of a number of statements about our solar system.

not to scale

For each statement, say whether it is **true or false**, and give a **reason** for your decision.

a) The Sun makes energy by changing hydrogen gas into water.

b) All the planets are visible because of light they produce themselves.

c) The Moon orbits the Earth.

d) The planets in the solar system orbit around a massive object.

e) The motion of planets, comets and satellites is determined by gravity.

f) All planets have spherical orbits.

g) Stars in other solar systems look dim because they are smaller than the Sun.

Q2 The diagram below shows the outer planets of our solar system.

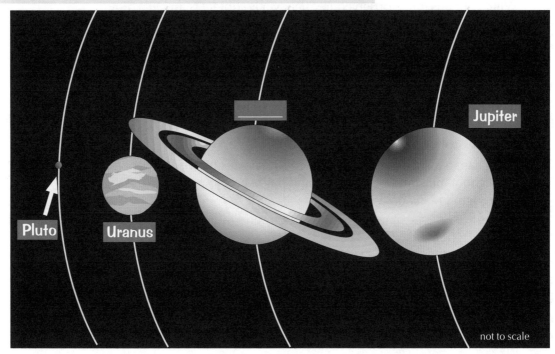

Jupiter

Pluto Uranus

not to scale

a) One planet's name has been left out. **Redraw the diagram** and add the missing name.

b) One planet has been missed from the diagram altogether. **Sketch in the orbit** on your diagram, and label it with the planet's name.

The Universe and its Origin

Q1   List the objects below in order of **size**, starting with the smallest.

Planet

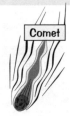
Comet

Star

Meteorite

Galaxy

Q2   We know quite a lot about the Universe and how it is changing.

Name and describe the **theory** that best explains how the Universe began and continues to evolve.

Q3   The following paragraph is about the **origin** and evolution of the Universe. **Fill in** the blanks using the given words.

theory	red shift	background radiation	explosion	Big Bang	evidence	expanding

Most astronomers now believe the Universe began with a huge explosion which we call the

_____ _____ . This theory is supported by strong scientific _____ . About 35 years

ago astronomers detected microwave _____ _____ coming from all directions in

space. This radiation is thought to have been released in the Big Bang. Also, by examining

the ____ _____ of the spectrums of stars, astronomers have discovered that the Universe is

_____ . The expansion of the Universe suggests that some sort of initial _____

took place . This is further evidence in support of the Big Bang _____ .

Q4   When an object moves relative to an observer, the frequency of the electromagnetic radiation received by the observer changes.

a)   What is the **name** of this effect?

b)   What happens to the observed frequency if an object is **approaching**?

c)   What happens to the observed frequency of an object that is **moving away**?

d)   **Give two examples** from everyday life of this effect in action.

Q5   The picture is a representation of part of a light wave emitted by a galaxy.

a)   Copy the wave, and show how it is changed by the galaxy's movement **away from us**.

b)   If the galaxy is replaced with a loudspeaker, describe what you would hear as it moves away with a **gradually increasing velocity**.

c)   This change to the light waves emitted by galaxies has been happening throughout the Universe's history, and has been happening to the background radiation as well.

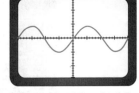

Suggest what type of radiation the background radiation was when the Universe was very young.

Q6   Decide whether each of these statements about the background radiation is **true** or **false**.

a)   The background radiation has a low frequency.

b)   The background radiation is coming from all directions.

c)   The background radiation comes from all parts of the Universe.

d)   The background radiation is ultra violet.

e)   The background radiation has changed since the Universe started.

f)   The background radiation was created well after the beginning of the Universe.

g)   The background radiation is microwave radiation.

h)   If we travelled to another part of the Universe, the background radiation would be the same.

The Life Cycle of Stars

Q1 Astronomers have been studying groups of stars. They have used their observations to come up with an idea for how they think some of the stars evolved.

This "Life Cycle" is illustrated in the diagram below:

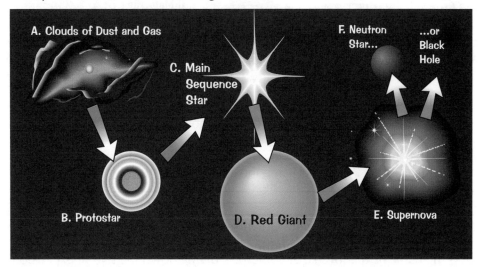

a) What **type of star** follows this life cycle?

b) Why are stars visible to us, even though they are so far away?

c) The scientists' ideas about stages A and B above are uncertain. Suggest why it is difficult to find **evidence** about these stages.

d) At a certain stage in the life-cycle, the temperature inside a star exerts an outward force. There's also a force acting **towards the centre** of the star. What **causes** it?

e) At which stage in the cycle do these forces balance each other?

f) In the diagram above, many **heavier atoms** are made just before which stage?

g) What is happening to make the red giant star **redder** than a main sequence star?

h) How does the matter making up neutron stars and black holes **differ** from the matter we are used to on Earth?

i) **Explain why** astronomers need to study a group of stars rather than just one or two, when studying life cycles.

j) What is the process in which **energy** can be created when atoms are forced together?

Q2 Medium–weight stars, such as the **Sun**, follow a different life cycle once they have reached the red giant stage. Even then, **two** different things can happen.

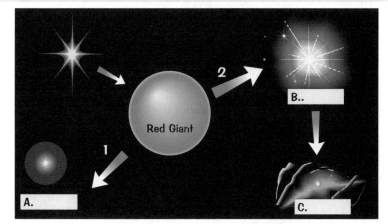

a) The **smaller** medium-weight stars (like the Sun) follow route 1. Name the object labelled A.

b) The **larger** medium-weight stars follow route 2. Complete the label at position B.

c) What is object C? What might happen to it over the course of time?

The Future of the Universe

Q1   Two factors help to determine how the Universe evolves.

   a)   What are these two factors?

   b)   One of them is **relatively easy** to measure, one is a **lot more difficult**. Which is which?

Q2   Measuring the total amount of mass in the Universe is not easy. Some matter is easy to see because it shines, and scientists can measure its mass. The rest is difficult, because we just can't see it. For each of the objects below, choose which are **visible** and which are **invisible**.

> *Supergiant Stars   Interstellar Dust   White Dwarf Stars*
>
> *Black Holes   Black Dwarves*
>
> *Main Sequence Stars   Dust between the Galaxies*

Q3   The Universe is expanding — we can be sure of this much.

   a)   What is the **name of the force** that could be slowing down the rate of expansion?

   b)   If there were no forces acting, how would the Universe continue to evolve?

Q4   Scientists love drawing graphs to show what is happening in the Universe.
The graph below shows what has happened to the size of the Universe up to now.

   a)   The curve on the graph opposite is not a straight line but rises less and less steeply. What does this tell us about the expansion of the Universe?

   b)   On two copies of this graph, sketch the two possible futures for how the Universe might evolve from now on.

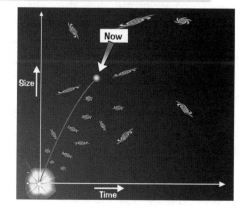

Q5   Complete the paragraph using the following words:

Universe   Solar System   4.5 billion years   radioactivity   Universe   2 billion years   Moon   Earth

> The first calculations made by scientists about the age of the _____ gave an age of only
> _____. This result was a big surprise because previous _____ measurements on rocks
> from the _____ (and later the _____) showed the age of the Solar System to be about
> _____. The _____ can't be older than the _____!

Q6   The end of the world as we know it...

   a)   What is the "**Big Crunch**"?

   b)   If the Big Crunch occurs, **how long** (at least...) have we got before it happens?

Q7   Make another copy of the graph in Question 4. This time, extend it so that it illustrates a **cyclical Universe** — one that expands, then contracts, and then expands again.

Searching for Life on Other Planets

We may not be alone in the Universe — there may well be life elsewhere.
Scientists are using a variety of methods to try and find evidence of extraterrestrial life.

Q1 There are certain **conditions** that are necessary for **life** to exist on other planets.
Fill in the blank spaces on the diagram below, using these words:

temperature	hot	UV radiation	water	cold	pressures	liquid

It's essential that there's _____ in _____ form.

The _____ must be just right — not too ____ and not too ____.

Life can't exist in extreme atmospheric _____.

A suitable atmosphere is required. It protects life from harmful _____.

Q2 The scientists at **SETI** are searching for intelligent life on other planets.

a) **What** does SETI stand for? Explain fully what SETI does.

b) **How** would SETI astronomers know that a radio signal was from a specially made transmitter?

Q3 The SETI programme is not the only way in which scientists are looking for evidence of life on **other planets**.

Complete this passage by filling in the blank spaces.

life	Mars	spacecraft	bacteria	missions	solar	system	extraterrestrial
	meteorites	fossils	stars	microscopes	telescopes	evidence	

Scientists are searching for life on other planets and moons in our _____ by sending _____ to them. There have been some _____ to Mars, for example, which have involved both orbiting and landing craft, both looking for any tell-tale signs of _____.

Studying _____, rocks which have fallen to Earth from space, is another way in which scientists are searching for signs of _____ life.
Quite recently, scientists analysed a meteorite from _____ using high-powered _____. They found what could possibly be small _____ of ancient Martian _____.

Astronomers are also using _____ to search for other _____ with planets orbiting them. There is now strong _____ to suggest that such planets have been found.

The Three Types of Radiation

Q1   There are 3 different types of **nuclear radiation** — alpha, beta and gamma.

Do the following apply to:

1) ALPHA RADIATION (α)?

2) BETA RADIATION (β)?

3) GAMMA RADIATION (γ)?

4) ALL THREE?

a) Is the **most penetrating** type of radiation.

b) Is the **least penetrating** type of radiation.

c) Can't pass through a thick sheet of **card**.

d) Can't pass through 1 metre of **lead**.

e) Can pass through a thick sheet of card but is blocked by 5mm of **aluminium**.

f) Consists of small **negatively-charged particles**.

g) Is an uncharged **electromagnetic wave**.

h) Consists of massive **positively-charged particles**.

i) Consists of fast-moving **electrons**.

j) Consists of **helium nuclei**.

k) Can damage **living cells**.

Q2   There are many useful **applications** of nuclear radiation. **Copy** the words from the following boxes and then use arrows to join each application to the type of radiation it uses.

medical tracers

testing paper thickness

Alpha (α)	Beta (β)	Gamma (γ)

treating cancer

sterilising equipment

smoke detectors

Q3   The following paragraph is about the **background nuclear radiation** on Earth. **Fill in** the blank spaces using the given words.

exposed	cosmic rays	rocks	background	natural	soil	radioactive	outer space

Throughout our daily lives we are all _____ to nuclear radiation from _____ sources. This is commonly called _____ radiation. Some of this radiation comes from the _____ and _____ around us. This is because they both contain small amounts of _____ substances. Another source of background radiation is _____. Radiation called _____ bombards the earth and adds to the natural radiation levels.

Radioactivity and Half-Life

Q1 When radiation travels through matter it can cause ionisation.

  a) Explain what is meant by the term "**ionisation**".

The diagram below shows a simplified drawing of an
experiment to demonstrate that radiation can ionise matter.

The space between the plates is filled with
argon gas at low pressure.
A current is measured.

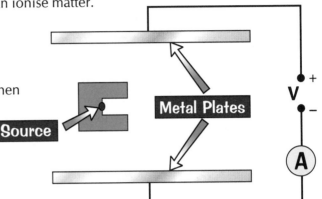

  b) What happens to some of the argon atoms when
the radioactive source is exposed?

  c) **Describe** how this leads to a
current in the circuit.

  d) The argon gas is removed from
between the plates, leaving a vacuum
behind. **Explain** why there is now no current flow.

Q2 **Copy and complete** the following sentences about the half-life of radioactive atoms.

zero   time   half   atoms   radioactivity   gamma   alpha
beta   nucleus   decreases   decay
The _____ of a sample always _____ over time. Each time a decay happens, _____, _____ or _____ radiation is emitted. This means a radioactive _____ has decayed. The problem with trying to measure the time for all the atoms to decay is that the activity never reaches _____. The half-life is the _____ taken for _____ of the radioactive _____ now present to _____.

Q3 Below is a table showing how the count rate decreases with time for a sample of polonium-218.

Count rate in counts per second	390	307	240	194	156	123	96
Time in minutes	0	1	2	3	4	5	6

  a) Using the data in the table, **plot a graph** of count rate (vertical axis)
against time (horizontal axis).

  b) Using your graph, **estimate** the half-life of polonium-218.

Q4 A sample of a radioactive substance was found to be emitting 8000 beta particles a second at the
beginning of an experiment. Fifteen minutes later, it was emitting 4000 beta particles a second.

  a) What is the **half-life** of the radioactive substance?

  b) **How many minutes** after the start would you expect to measure
a count rate of 1000 particles per second?

  c) What count rate would you expect to measure after **two hours**?

  d) Background radiation from radioactive materials in the ground or in the
air is about 2 counts per second. How long would it take the count rate
from the substance to fall **below this background count**?

88

Radioactivity and Half-Life

Q1 The count rate from a radioactive material was measured using a G-M tube and counter. These are the results below:

Count rate in counts per second	95	73	55	42	32	23	18
Time in seconds	0	10	20	30	40	50	60

a) **Plot a graph** of count rate in counts / second (vertical axis) against time in seconds (horizontal axis).

b) **Find the half-life** of the material by finding how long it took the count rate to fall from 90 to 45.

c) Another material has a very low activity which makes it difficult to measure its activity above the background radiation. **Describe** how you might overcome this problem.

Q2 Igneous rocks can be dated if you measure the ratios of uranium-238 and its decay product lead. The half-life of uranium-238 is 4.5 billion years. Assuming no lead was present when the rocks were formed, **find the ages of the rocks** in a) and b) using the given ratios:

a) Uranium : lead is 1 : 1   **b)** Uranium : lead is 1 : 0

Q3 Lead-210 (atomic number 82) decays with the emission of a beta particle. Bismuth-210 is formed, which decays with the emission of a beta-particle to form polonium-210.

a) Write down a **symbol equation** for the above decay series, showing the mass and atomic numbers for all the atoms.

b) The graph opposite shows how the activity of bismuth-210 varies with time. **Estimate** the half-life of bismuth-210.

c) Polonium-210 decays with the emission of an α-particle. An isotope of lead is formed. What is the **mass number** of this isotope of lead?

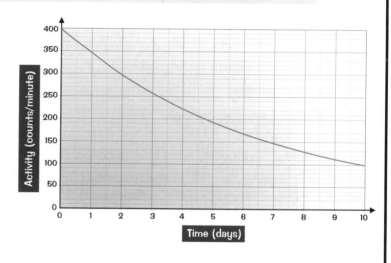

Q4 The table below shows how the activity of a radioactive source changes with time. The background count rate was determined to be 10 counts per **minute**.

Time(s)	5	10	15	20	25	30	35	40	45	50	55	60	65	70	75
Activity(counts/s)	100	76	68	64	56	50	44	38	32	28	26	22	20	16	14

a) Use the data to **estimate the half-life** of the radioactive source.

b) The background radiation was measured over a long time. **Explain why** this is necessary.

Top Tips

All this stuff is really important so you've got to make sure you can do it. The examiners are especially keen on applications of all this stuff, so pay attention to the bit on isotope dating.

Module PD6 — Earth, Space and Nuclear Radiation

Answers — Module BD4

Module BD4 — Variation, Inheritance and Evolution

Page 1 — Variation

Q1 a) i) a and c
  ii) They are the only two that have all the same genetic features (roll tongue, brown hair, brown eyes and both male).
  b) i) Ability to tan; hair colour **ii)** Sex, tongue rolling, eye colour.

Q2 Inherited, environmental, discontinuous.

Q3 a) Chromosomes are found in the nucleus of body cells.
  b) Twenty-three.
  c) Hair colour, blood group, inherited diseases, eye colour.
  d) The other characteristics are affected by environmental factors.

Q4 a) i) weight, intelligence, height, hair colour, fitness
  ii) eye colour
  b) i) weight, intelligence, height, hair colour, fitness
  ii) eye colour
  c) Fitness
  d) Fitness — exercise; Intelligence — education; Hair colour — sunlight; Height and Weight — diet.

Page 2 — Variation

Q5 a) asexual
  b) two
  c) the same
  d) reduction, halved
  e) meiosis, gametes
  f) meiosis

Q6 a)

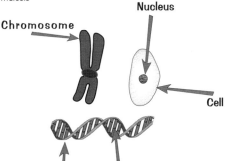

Nucleus

Chromosome

Cell

DNA is coiled up to make the chromosome

A gene is a short length of DNA

  b) Genes give chemical instructions to cells to determine how they grow. Different instructions produce different cells with different characteristics. A gene instruction for black hair will be not be the same as a gene instruction for blonde hair and will produce different cells.
  c) Divide, new, identical, divide, multiply, replicating, growth, replace.

Q7 a) F (nucleus) **b)** T **c)** F (chromosomes)
  d) F (haploid) **e)** T **f)** T **g)** T

Q8 a) Nucleus
  b) Genetic information is carried as genes.
  c) 46 (i.e. 23 pairs)
  d) DNA

Page 3 — Mutations

Q1 Chromosome, naturally, replication, nucleus, divide, mutations, ionising, mutagens, carcinogens, harmful, sex, mitosis, neutral, beneficial, antibiotics, genetic.

Q2 a) Sunlight contains harmful ultraviolet light, which can cause skin cancer and sunburn.
  b) The radiographer must stand behind a protective screen to prevent exposure to harmful X-rays.
  c) Carbon tetrachloride is a chemical that was found to be carcinogenic.
  d) Workers used to form an accurate point to their brushes by sucking the ends to a point in their mouths.

Q3

Organism	Number of chromosomes in a body cell	Number of pairs of chromosomes	Number of chromosomes in each gamete
Fruit Fly	8	4	4
Kangaroo	12	6	6
Rye Plant	20	10	10
Chicken	36	18	18
Mouse	40	20	20
Humans	46	23	23
Crayfish	200	100	100

Page 4 — Ordinary Cell Division: Mitosis

Q1

Asexual Reproduction	Sexual Reproduction
Offspring are clones of parent	Offspring are not genetically identical to parents
Only one parent is needed	Two parents are needed
No joining of sex cells needed	Male and female gametes join

Q2 A 1: Initially the DNA is spread out in long strings.
  2: Chromosomes are formed by the organisation of DNA strands. The double arms of the chromosome structure are duplicates of each other.
  3: The chromosomes line up along the centre of the cell and cell fibres pull them apart to opposite poles of the cell.
  4: Membranes begin to form, surrounding the two sets of chromosome sections produced in stage three. These become the nuclei of the two daughter cells.
  5: Two separate cells are produced, identical to the parent cell in stage one. The threads begin to unwind and become evenly distributed within the nucleus.

  B 1: The chromosomes pair up. There are 46 human chromosomes so there are 23 pairs. In each pair one chromosome is from your mother the other is from your father.
  2: The pairs of chromosomes now split up and go to opposite poles of the cell. The two nuclei produced from this splitting are different, containing a mixture of chromosomes from both your mother and father.
  3: The chromosomes themselves now split forming duplicates of themselves within two nucleii.
  4: There are now two sets of duplicate cell pairs produced when the chromosomes split in stage three. The cells are called gametes.

Page 5 — Fertilisation: The Meeting of Gametes

Q1 a) See diagram:

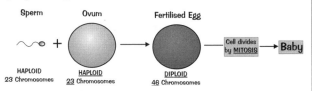

Sperm Ovum Fertilised Egg

Cell divides by MITOSIS → Baby

HAPLOID 23 Chromosomes HAPLOID 23 Chromosomes DIPLOID 46 Chromosomes

  b) i) testes **ii)** ovaries
  c) gametes
  d) zygote
  e) fertilisation
  f) oviduct / Fallopian tube

Q2 gametes, fertilisation, meiosis, variation, egg, children, sperm, ova, testes, ovaries, chromosome, diploid.

Answers — Module BD4

Page 6 — Cloned Plants

Q1 a) Asexual
  b) i) They have the same genes. **ii)** Clones.
  c) i) New plants can be produced quickly; need less space; can grow all year round; new plants are disease free; easier to harvest.
  ii) Reduce gene pool, so plants are vulnerable to diseases.
  d) Taking cuttings.

Q2 a) Asexual
  b) Damp atmosphere until the roots develop.
  c) They are genetically identical.
  d) They are different.
  e) i) New plants are produced quickly, identical to parent plant.
  ii) Less variety, reduction in gene pool.

Q3 a) mitotic
  b) identical
  c) asexual
  d) decreases
  e) before
  f) large; aseptic

Page 7 — Cloned Plants

Q4 Genetically, asexual, mitosis, cuttings, tissue, identical, cells, splitting, embryo, host, naturally.

Q5 a) Mitosis
  b) Because they are genetically identical to each other.
  c) i) Fast, produces offspring identical to each other (so you can breed from a prize cow and a prize bull over and over again in a very short space of time).
  ii) Reduces variety of genes in the gene pool.

Q6 a) False — plants produce exact copies of themselves by asexual reproduction.
  b) True.
  c) False — asexual reproduction produces less variation than sexual reproduction.
  d) False — sexual reproduction requires two parents.
  e) True.

Page 8 — Monohybrid Crosses: Terminology

Q1a) DNA,
  b) chromatids
  c) in the middle of the chromosome
  d) a gene is a section of DNA
  e) dominant
  f) homozygous means that the person has two identical alleles
  g) the characteristic of the dominant allele

Q2 **a)** See diagram:

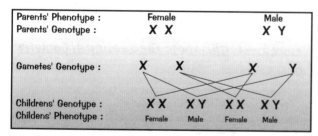

b) 50:50 / 2:2 / 1:1
c) No, every time a woman conceives there is a 50:50 chance of a boy/girl being born.

d) See diagram:

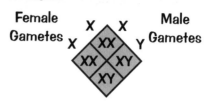

Q3 a) X or Y
  b) X
  c) i) Man's gamete.
  ii) Sex of the child depends on whether an X or Y bearing sperm fuses with the egg.

Page 9 — Monohybrid Crosses: Terminology

Q4 a) Both alleles are the same.
  b) Because B is a dominant gene, b is recessive.
  c) They determine the same characteristic, i.e. colour.
  d) i) First generation of offspring. **ii)** Two different alleles.
  e) i) B **ii)** It 'dominates' or masks a recessive allele.
  f) i) The genes present **ii)** Appearance/physical characteristics
  g) i)

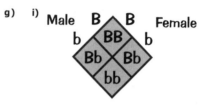

  ii) Phenotypes: black, brown. Genotypes: BB, Bb, bb.
  iii) 3 black : 1 brown **iv)** F2

Q5 a) B — brown and b — blue (any sensible choice).
  b)

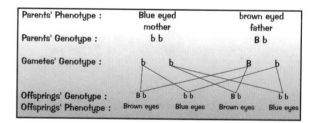

c) Mother (bb); the offspring with genotype bb
d) Brown eyed parents may carry the gene for blue eyes, so the blue eyed child would have inherited one recessive 'blue eye gene' from each parent.

Q6 monohybrid, height, alleles, recessive, homozygous, heterozygous, phenotype, genotype, F1, F2.

Page 10 — Genetic Diseases

Q1 Genetic, recessive, membranes, allele, both, carriers

Q2 a) i) Cc
  ii) cc
  iii) CC and cc
  iv) Cc
  b) They carry recessive alleles, but are not sufferers.

Q3 a) Cystic fibrosis is an **inherited** disease.
  b) Cystic fibrosis is caused by a **recessive** allele
  c) Children can inherit the cystic fibrosis disease when **both** of their parents have the recessive allele.

Answers — Modules BD4 and BD5

Page 11 — Genetic Diseases

Q4 a) Father = Cc, Mother = CC.
b) No
c) i) No
ii) Each one has a 50% chance of carrying the disease.
d) 50%
e) 50%
f) i) No
ii) He could have the same genotype whether one or both parents were carriers.

Q5 a) red blood cells
b) the red blood cells are less efficient at carrying oxygen, and tend to stick together in the blood capillaries. This deprives the body cells of oxygen.
c) sickle cell anaemia is carried by a recessive allele, so someone with the disease must have two sickle cell alleles.
d) no — but their children may carry the disease.

Q6 a) Since the carriers of the sickle cell allele are more immune to malaria, more people with this allele will survive in malaria infected areas. Hence the high distribution of the allele in these areas.
b) i) They are protected against malaria.
ii) Their offspring may develop the disease.

Q7 a) Advantage. Useful biological products can be produced. Disadvantage. The long term effects are largely unknown.
b) Genetic engineering allows scientists to 'play God', and create organisms which wouldn't naturally exist.

Page 12 — Selective Breeding / Genetic Engineering

Q1 a) True
b) False, individuals with the desired characteristics are identified and used for breeding.
c) True
d) False, Friesian cows now produce higher milk yields.
e) True
f) True
g) False, because the animals or crops are constantly bred with each other, harmful recessive characteristics accumulate.
h) False, inbreeding reduces the gene pool, and can develop characteristics which are harmful to the individual.

Q2 a) Pointed ears, long tail, long hair, sticking up ears, pointed snout, etc.
b) Have greater variety of alleles — haven't been selected for aesthetic purposes which sacrifice health.
c) The breed would eventually disappear.

Q3 a) artificial
b) decreases
c) increase
d) sexual
e) disadvantageous

Page 13 — Fossils and Evolution

Q1 changed, Darwin, adaptations, environment, inherit, organisms, food, fittest, characteristics, nature, survival, natural, evolution.

Q2 All giraffes had short necks; mutation resulted in some giraffes having longer necks than others; the giraffe population had individuals whose necks varied in length; natural selection resulted in longer-necked offspring surviving; only long-necked giraffes survived the competition for food.

Page 14 — Natural Selection

Q1 a) True.
b) False, animals that adapt well to their environment are more likely to survive.
c) True.

Q2 a) decay; sediment — Stage A
b) animal — Stage C
c) decay; minerals — Stage B
d) bones; teeth; shells — Stage D

Q3 a) Fish
b) Mammals
c) They show changes and development of organisms over millions of years.
d) Fossilisation is rare / did not occur.

Module BD5 — The Working Plant

Page 15 — Photosynthesis

Q1 a) Clockwise from top left — oxygen is released into the atmosphere, (sun)light for energy is absorbed by chlorophyll, water from the soil, carbon dioxide from the atmosphere.
b) Photosynthesis.
c) Starch / sugar / glucose.

Q2 a) Word equation:

$$\text{Carbon dioxide} + \text{water} \xrightarrow[\substack{\text{absorbed by}\\\text{chlorophyll}}]{\text{light/solar energy}} \text{glucose} + \text{oxygen}$$

b) Chemical equation:

$$6CO_2 + 6H_2O \xrightarrow[\substack{\text{absorbed by}\\\text{chlorophyll}}]{\text{light/solar energy}} C_6H_{12}O_6 + 6O_2$$

Q3 a) The green cells have choroplasts; white cells do not.
b) Chlorophyll.

Q4 a) Lack of oxygen.
b) Carbon dioxide.

Page 16 — Photosynthesis

Q5 a) Lower surface is on the water. It's very difficult to get gases from water. The plant needs CO_2 from the air, so it needs pores on the upper surface.
b) Carbon dioxide.
c) Large surface area of leaf.

Q6 a) Leaves are thin from top to bottom so that light reaches all the palisade cells. Light is needed for photosynthesis.
b) Leaves contain chlorophyll. They have a network of veins to provide water. They are broad to absorb lots of light.
c) Transparent epidermis lets light enter the leaf. Palisade layer at the top of the leaf contains most of the chloroplasts, and catches lots of sunlight in this position. Air spaces in the mesophyll are connected to the stomata so that gases can enter the leaf and take part in photosynthetic reactions. Internal surface area to volume ratio is very large, so gases can quickly diffuse into and out of the leaf.

Q7 a) The influence that most restricts the rate of a reaction.
b) Temperature / concentration of carbon dioxide.
c) Curve drawn higher up than but parallel with other two curves (but coinciding with them at the origin).
d) Summer.

Q8 a) Other soluble sugars. **b)** Insoluble starch.

Q9 a) Converted into cellulose for making cell walls. Combined with nitrates to form amino acids, which are then built up into proteins.
b) Turned into lipids (fats and oils) for storage in seeds.

Page 17 — Photosynthesis

Q10a) i) Transport of water and food (sugar); provides support for leaf.
ii) Xylem for water transport, Phloem for sugar transport. Xylem and Phloem for support.
b) i) To allow gases to diffuse into and out of the leaf.
ii) Amount of water in (OR turgidity of) guard cells.
iii) To reduce water loss.

The Answers

Answers — Modules BD5 and BD6

c) i) Palisade cell.
   ii) To make food (sugar) / photosynthesis.
   iii) Has many chloroplasts for lots of photosynthesis / has cylindrical shape for strength.
d) i) (Spongy) mesophyll cell.
   ii) Gases can diffuse through spaces.
e) Reduce/stop water loss.

Q11   A — i), B — iii), C — ii), D — iv).

Q12   palisade, chloroplasts, chlorophyll, mesophyll, carbon dioxide, xylem, veins, waxy cuticle, stomata, guard cells.

Page 18 — Diffusion

Q1   Carbon dioxide enters leaves and cells by diffusion.

Q2   Osmosis is the movement of water molecules from a region of high water concentration to a region of low water concentration across a differentially permeable membrane. Osmosis can be considered as a special case of diffusion.

Q3 a) The pressure inside a cell increases when water moves into it.
   b) This increase in pressure keeps the cell rigid (maintains its turgor pressure) and hence provides support.
   c) The inelastic wall won't bend or stretch, so the cells keep their shape.
   d) If there is no water in the soil, the cells start to lose water and thus lose their turgor pressure.

Q4 a) The red ink from inside the Visking tubing diffuses into the water; it moves from a high to a low concentration of ink particles.
   b) Water moved into the Visking tubing by osmosis from a high concentration of water (lower concentration of sugar) to a lower concentration of water (higher concentration of sugar).

Q5 a) i) Osmosis.
      ii) Guard cells have a greater concentration of solute than the surrounding cells — this causes water to move into them from the surrounding cells.
   b) i) Oxygen, carbon dioxide (or water vapour). ii) Diffusion.
   c) i) In bright light glucose is produced in the guard cells by photosynthesis — water flows into the guard cells by osmosis. The cells become turgid and the stomatal pores open.
      ii) When water is plentiful, the cells become turgid and change shape, which opens the stomatal pores.

Page 19 — The Transpiration System

Q1 a) Xylem cells. The cells are hollow so that movement of their contents can occur.
   b) Minerals.
   c) Phloem cells. The cells are perforated to allow the movement of substances from cell to cell.
   d) Roots, stems, storage organs, shoot tips, root tips.
   e) The transported food consists of sugar (accept glucose or glucose/sucrose) and other food substances like fatty acids and amino acids.
   f) These tubes run alongside each other through the centre of stems. They pass through the centre of leaves and then spread out to supply products to the whole leaf.

Q2   Transpiration / evaporation, xylem, leaves, stomata, guard, lower, evaporation, temperature, greater, wilt, cuticle, thicker.

Q3 a) B.
   b) Moving air causes more evaporation from leaf surface by carrying newly evaporated moisture away from the leaf surface (so that a concentration gradient is maintained).
   c) Curve A resembles the response on a hot day. This is because both higher temperatures and moving air increase evaporation.

Page 20 — The Transpiration System

Q1 a) The lower surface. Anhydrous cobalt chloride (blue) turns pink in the presence of water. Water is lost from the stomata, which are on the lower surface of the leaf.
   b) Transpiration.

c) From the soil. (Through the roots/xylem are acceptable answers)
d) atmospheric humidity, low temperature, little wind.

Q2 a) Some is used in photosynthesis and for cell turgidity.
   b) Evaporation.
   c) Xylem.
   d) Minerals / nutrients.

Q3 a) To reduce water loss.
   b) The guard cells control the opening and closing of the stomata. The pores are open when the guard cells are turgid, but closed when they are flaccid (when they have lost water), thus reducing further water loss.

Q4 a) i) A.
      ii) Similar number of stomata on both surfaces.
   b) Allow transpiration; allow gaseous exchange; control rates of transpiration / gaseous exchange.
   c) i) Any of these: light, temperature, humidity, wind movements.
      ii) Affects size of pore, according to whether the guard cell remains turgid (to keep the pore open), or becomes flaccid due to water loss (closing the pore).

Page 21 — Minerals and Fertilisers

Q1 a) They have a projection/extension — increases surface area for absorption of water/minerals.
   b) Sap vacuole, cell wall.

Q2   In order they appear: higher, soil, diffusion, active, transport, concentration, gradient, growth, active, transport, respiration.

Q3   Nitrates, protein, magnesium, fertiliser, phosphate, potassium.

Module BD6 — Health in the Balance

Page 22 — Respiration

Q1   See table:

GAS	% in inhaled air	% in exhaled air
oxygen	21	16
carbon dioxide	0.04	4
nitrogen	78	78

Q2 a) glucose + oxygen → carbon dioxide + water (+ energy transferred).
   b) $C_6H_{12}O_6 + 6O_2 \rightarrow 6CO_2 + 6H_2O$ + energy transferred.
   c) Glucose and oxygen are needed for respiration. They are transported to the cells in the bloodstream. Glucose comes from food (digested in the digestive system and absorbed through the walls of the small intestine into the bloodstream). Oxygen comes from air (inhaled into the lungs and absorbed through the walls of the alveoli into the bloodstream).
   d) Carbon dioxide and water are produced by respiration. Carbon dioxide and water diffuse from the cells into the bloodstream through the walls of the capillaries. They will diffuse from the bloodstream into the alveoli (in the lungs), again through capillaries, and are then passed out of the body as exhaled air. Water also leaves the body in urine, faeces and sweat.
   e) Energy is produced by respiration.

Q3   In order they appear: incomplete, glucose, incomplete, less, aerobic, oxygen debt, oxidise, carbon dioxide, water.

Q4   **Aerobic Respiration**:
           Uses glucose and oxygen.
           Produces carbon dioxide and water.
           Releases energy.
        Anaerobic Respiration:
           Produces lactic acid.
           Results in an oxygen debt.
           Releases energy.
           Uses glucose.
           Releases the least energy.

Answers — Module BD6

Page 23 — Respiration

Q5 a) Because the muscles are using up more oxygen than his body can supply. When the oxygen supply has been used up, his muscles begin to respire anaerobically, producing lactic acid. The build up of lactic acid causes the pain he feels, and makes him unable to continue clenching.

b) David's hand muscles receive more blood, and therefore more oxygen, than when raised. More blood reaching the muscles also means more waste products are taken away. This allows the muscles to contract more often before the build-up of lactic acid from anaerobic respiration becomes too high.

Q6 a) Aerobic respiration.
b) When Georgina begins to run, her muscles contract more frequently. This additional muscular activity needs energy from respiration. More oxygen is needed to allow aerobic respiration to continue at a greater rate than when she was resting, so oxygen uptake increases.
c) There is a limit to how much air can be taken in by breathing, how much gaseous exchange can take place in the lungs, and how much oxygen can be transported to the respiring cells by the blood.
d) During the race, more energy is required for muscular contraction than can be supplied by aerobic respiration alone, so anaerobic respiration occurs. The product of anaerobic respiration is lactic acid, and this builds up in her body.
e) After the race, less energy is needed for muscular contraction. The additional oxygen being taken in can be used to oxidise the lactic acid to carbon dioxide and water. This continues until it is all oxidised, with the rate of oxygen uptake gradually returning to normal.
f) The oxygen debt is the volume of oxygen needed to oxidise all the lactic acid produced by anaerobic respiration.

Q7 The brain detects the carbon dioxide levels in the blood. If they are too high then the brain initiates an increase in breathing rate.

Page 24 — Maintaining Conditions

Q1 37°C.

Q2 thermoregulatory, centre, receptors, temperature, receptors, impulses, skin, temperature.

Q3 a) In order they are: dilate, more, constrict, less.
b) Another way in which the body cools itself down is by sweating. The sweat glands release more sweat which cools the body as it evaporates.
c) When muscles shiver, they contract. This process needs respiration which releases some energy as heat.

Q4 a) Most carbon dioxide leaves the body via the lungs when we breathe out.
b) Urea is removed by the kidneys in the urine.

Q5 a) Water content of the body, ion content of the body and temperature.
b) Water leaves the body via the lungs when we breathe out and via the skin when we sweat. Excess is lost via the kidneys in the urine.
c) Ions are lost via the skin when we sweat. Excess ions are lost via the kidneys in the urine.

Page 25 — Kidneys and Homeostasis

Q1 a) A — kidney / B — renal vein / C — renal artery / D — ureter / E — bladder / F — urethra.
b) Renal artery carries oxygenated blood and the renal vein carries de-oxygenated blood.

Q2 In order they appear: food, drink, blood, kidneys, urine, faeces, sweat, breath, brain, sweat, more, dark, less, pale, dilute.

Q3 Homeostasis is maintaining a constant internal environment, which involves balancing all the bodily inputs and outputs.

Q4 a) Negative Feedback
b) Negative feedback is when something happens that triggers a new process that inhibits the original action.

c) The regulation of the glucose content of the blood.

Page 26 — Fighting Diseases

Q1 Unhygienic conditions; contact with infected people; entry point into the body for microorganisms, eg. cuts to skin.

Q2 Any of: unbroken skin; clotting of the blood to seal the wound; white cells (phagocytes to ingest bacteria; lymphocytes to produce antibodies); mucus and cilia in respiratory tract, acid in stomach.

Q3 White cells protect us against infection by: engulfing microbes; producing antibodies; producing antitoxins.

Q4 A - Microbes, B - White blood cell, C - New microbe, D - Antibodies produced.

Q5 The two types of microbe are bacteria and viruses.

Q6 immunised, mild, dead, organism, white, antibodies, organism, antibodies, bacterium, virus, immune.

Page 27 — Drugs

Q1 a) Drugs change the **chemical** processes in people's bodies so that they may become **dependent** or **addicted** to them.
b) Withdrawal symptoms.
Three of: nausea; fevers; hallucinations and the shakes.
c) Because their tolerance to the drug increases so they need more to get the same effect each time.

Q2 a) The nervous system.
b) It affects behaviour by slowing down the nervous system and can give the individual more confidence. Causes lack of self-control and can lead to unconsciousness or even coma.

Q3 Liver and brain.

Q4 a) Nicotine
b) Bronchitis and emphysema.
c) These diseases lead to heart attacks and strokes.
d) The tar from cigarettes affects the cilia which remove mucus from the lungs. If the mucus can't be removed by the cilia, then it has to be coughed up.

Q5 a) Carbon monoxide reduces the oxygen-carrying capacity of the blood, by combining with the haemoglobin in red blood cells. This puts a strain on the heart.
b) In pregnant women, this can deprive a foetus of oxygen and lead to a low birth mass.

Q6 The cells may carry on dividing and form a lump called a tumour — lung cancer.

Page 28 — Drugs

Q7 Tobacco — Lungs, heart and blood vessels.
Alcohol — Liver and brain.
Solvents — Lungs, liver and brain.

Q8 a) **(i)** Alcohol is used for **relaxation**.
(ii) It **slows down** the brain and can make you feel less **inhibited**.
(iii) However, excessive drinking can lead to damage to the **liver** and a drop in **brain** function.
b) The more alcohol taken in, the poorer a driver's judgement becomes. His/her reactions are slower and this results in an increased risk of them causing an accident.

Q9 a) Stimulants speed up brain activity.
b) Depressants slow down brain activity.

Q10 a) Hallucinations and personality change.
b) Stopping taking drugs like amphetamines causes severe depression. This is a psychological, rather than physical addiction.

Answers — Modules BD6 and CD4

Q11 Solvents inhibit the transmission of impulses at the synapses of the nervous system. This can slow down your reactions and make you less responsive.

CD4 —Carbon chemistry

Page 29 — Covalent Bonding

Q1

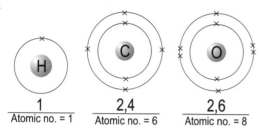

Q2 A molecule is a group of atoms bonded together and capable of free existence.

Q3 Bonding.

Q4 One or more pairs of electrons.

Q5

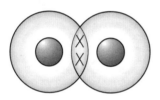

Q6 So they have a more stable, full outer shell of electrons.

Q7

a) Carbon Dioxide (CO_2)

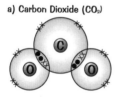

b) Water (H_2O)

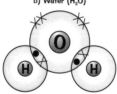

c) Hydrogen (H_2)

d) Ethene (C_2H_4)

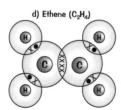

e) Methane (CH_4)

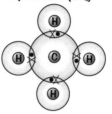

f) Chlorine (Cl_2)

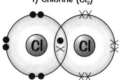

Q8 a) Low, gas, liquid, do not.
b) Carbon dioxide and water are simple molecules with weak intermolecular forces. These weak intermolecular forces mean they have low melting points and no free electrons, so don't conduct electricity.

Page 30 — Structures

Q1 a) Diamond
b) Graphite
c) Buckminster Fullerene

Q2 atoms, large, high, diamond, graphite, carbon, four, rigid, hard, three, layers, slide, soft, lubricant, no, one, delocalised, graphite, diamond.

Page 31 — Alkanes

Q1 C_nH_{2n+2}

Q2

Name	Formula	Number of Carbons	Melting Point (°C)	Boiling Point (°C)	Structural (graphical) Formula
Methane	CH_4	1	-182	-164	
Ethane	C_2H_6	2	-183	-89	
Propane	C_3H_8	3	-190	-42	
Butane	C_4H_{10}	4	-138	0	
Pentane	C_5H_{12}	5	-130	36	
Hexane	C_6H_{14}	6	-95	69	
Heptane	C_7H_{16}	7	-91	98	
Octane	C_8H_{18}	8	-57	126	
Nonane	C_9H_{20}	9	-51	151	
Decane	$C_{10}H_{22}$	10	-30	174	

Q3 a) Hydrocarbons.
b) The two atoms in the bond share one pair of electrons.
c) That the molecule contains no double or triple bonds.
d) The bromine water stays brown.
e) Cracking.
f) Many more products (eg plastics) can be made from them.

Answers — Module CD4

Page 32 — Alkenes

Q1 a) They have a double or triple bond and so have spare electrons available to bond.

b) They can react with other chemicals, and polymerise.

Q2 a) Because they have spare electrons available to bond. The double bond can break apart and add on other elements.

b)i) $C_2H_4 + H_2 \rightarrow C_2H_6$

ii)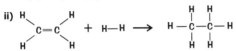

iii) Ethane.

iv) Catalyst (usually nickel) and high pressure.

v) Hydrogenation.

c) $C_3H_6 + H_2 \rightarrow C_3H_8$

Q3 a) The ethene will decolourise the bromine water to form a clear solution.

b) $C_2H_4 + Br_2 \rightarrow C_2H_4Br_2$

c) $C_3H_6 + Br_2 \rightarrow C_3H_6Br_2$

d) Dibromo compound

Q4

Alkene	No. of Carbon atoms	Formula	Structural Formula
Ethene	2	C_2H_4	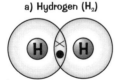
Propene	3	C_3H_6	

Page 33 — Hydrocarbons

Q1 Breaking complicated molecules down into simpler molecules by heating them. Long chain hydrocarbons aren't much use, but the shorter chain hydrocarbons are much more useful; shorter hydrocarbons are more expensive so profits are greater; greater demand for shorter chain hydrocarbons.

Q2 a) Hydrocarbons which contain a double bond between carbon atoms.

b) They have double or triple bonds, which means other chemicals will react easily with them.

c) Paraffin is saturated, and so cannot react with the bromine water. The gas A is an alkene — it's unsaturated and so it reacts with the bromine water and decolourises it.

d)

a) Hydrogen (H_2)

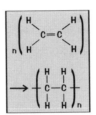

e) Ethene.

Q3 The large heavy fractions are not much use, but can be made useful by cracking them into smaller fractions. The smaller, lighter fractions are already useful.

Q4 a) Cracking (thermal decomposition).

b) To prevent the alkene produced reacting with the air.

c) C_2H_4 , C_6H_{12}

d) $C_{16}H_{34}$, C_6H_{14}

e) i) C_2H_4 , C_6H_{12}

ii) C_2H_4 , C_6H_{12}

f)

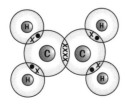

g) Making plastics, and other chemicals eg. petrol additives.

h) A polymer - poly(ethene).

i) Poly(vinylchloride) or poly(chloroethene) – PVC.

Q5 $C_8H_{18} \rightarrow C_4H_{10} + C_4H_8$

Page 34 — Polymers and Plastics

Q1 Lots of small units join up to make a long chain.

Q2 High pressure, a catalyst.

Q3 a) Poly(ethene) — polythene.

b)

$$n \begin{pmatrix} H & & H \\ & C = C & \\ H & & H \end{pmatrix} \rightarrow \begin{pmatrix} H & H \\ | & | \\ C - C \\ | & | \\ H & H \end{pmatrix}_n$$

c) Poly(ethene) — because it is made up of lots of molecules of ethene.

Q4 Polymerisation; carbon; addition; monomer; polymer; plastics; polythene; ethene; ethene monomers; high pressure; catalyst; double bonds; single.

Q5

Monomer	Name	Polymer	Name
a) $H_2C = CH$–CH_3	Propene	$\begin{pmatrix} H & H \\ C-C \\ H & CH_3 \end{pmatrix}_n$	Polypropene
b) $H_2C = CH$–(ring)	Styrene	$\begin{pmatrix} H & H \\ C-C \\ H & (ring) \end{pmatrix}_n$	Polystyrene
c) $H_2C = CH$–Cl	Chloroethene	$\begin{pmatrix} H & H \\ C-C \\ H & Cl \end{pmatrix}_n$	Polychloroethene

Page 35 — Uses of Plastics

Q1

Job	Plastic	Reason
Hot food container	Polystyrene	Can be expanded into foam
Plastic bags	Polythene	Cheap, easy to mould
Carpet	Polypropene	Forms strong fibres
Picnic glasses	Perspex	Does not easily shatter, transparent
Buckets	Polythene	Cheap, easy to mould
Ropes	Polypropene	Forms strong fibres
Bubble packing	Polythene	Cheap, easily to mould
Insulating material	Polystyrene	Can be expanded into foam
Yoghurt carton	Polythene	Cheap, easy to mould
Non-stick frying pans	PTFE	Waxy — things don't stick to it

Q2 Epoxy resins.

Q3 Plastics don't rot quickly (plastic bags will rot in about 50 years, but thick plastic bottles can take 10 000 years to rot!) so they're difficult to dispose of, because they don't burn very well either. If they are burnt they give off toxic fumes. Plastics can be buried in landfill, but that's a waste of resources, and you wouldn't want to cover too much land with landfill. Plastics can be recycled but it's expensive and difficult, since all the colours and types have to be separated.

Q4 Intermolecular bonds.

Answers — Modules CD4 and CD5

Q5 Weak bonds means that the polymer chains are free to slide over each other. This makes them easy to mould and gives them a low melting point. Stronger bonds result in a higher melting point and means they can't be stretched as easily. The stronger bonds are formed as crosslinks between the chains.

CD5 — Chemical Economics

Page 36 — Chemical Equations

Q1 a) Sodium + chlorine → **sodium chloride**
b) Carbon + **oxygen** → carbon dioxide
c) Sulphur + oxygen → **sulphur dioxide**
d) Zinc + oxygen → **zinc oxide**
e) **Iron + sulphur** → iron sulphide
f) Potassium + chlorine → **potassium chloride**
g) Lead + oxygen → **lead oxide**
h) **Calcium + oxygen** → calcium oxide

Q2 a) Iron sulphide.
b) Iron oxide.
c) Magnesium oxide.
d) Sulphur dioxide.
e) Water.
f) Magnesium sulphide.
g) Aluminium chloride.
h) Hydrogen iodide.
i) Carbon dioxide.

Q3 a) Gas, aqueous, solid.
b) (l) is also used. Liquid.

Page 37 — Balancing Equations

Q1 a) $C + O_2 \rightarrow CO_2$
b) $Zn + H_2SO_4 \rightarrow ZnSO_4 + H_2$
c) $Cu + Cl_2 \rightarrow CuCl_2$
d) $H_2 + CuO \rightarrow Cu + H_2O$
e) $Mg + H_2SO_4 \rightarrow MgSO_4 + H_2$

Q2 a) $N_2 + 3H_2 \rightarrow 2NH_3$
b) $CaCO_3 + H_2SO_4 \rightarrow CaSO_4 + H_2O + CO_2$
c) $2H_2 + O_2 \rightarrow 2H_2O$
d) $2Mg + O_2 \rightarrow 2MgO$
e) $Mg + H_2SO_4 \rightarrow MgSO_4 + H_2$
f) $H_2SO_4 + 2NaOH \rightarrow Na_2SO_4 + 2H_2O$
g) $Ca + H_2SO_4 \rightarrow CaSO_4 + H_2$
h) $H_2SO_4 + 2KOH \rightarrow K_2SO_4 + 2H_2O$
i) $Fe_2O_3 + 3CO \rightarrow 2Fe + 3CO_2$
j) $C_6H_{12}O_6 + 6O_2 \rightarrow 6CO_2 + 6H_2O$
k) $6CO_2 + 6H_2O \rightarrow C_6H_{12}O_6 + 6O_2$
l) $2C_4H_{10} + 13O_2 \rightarrow 8CO_2 + 10H_2O$
m) $C_2H_4 + 3O_2 \rightarrow 2CO_2 + 2H_2O$
n) $C_3H_8 + 5O_2 \rightarrow 3CO_2 + 4H_2O$
o) $C_5H_{12} + 8O_2 \rightarrow 5CO_2 + 6H_2O$
p) $2C_3H_6 + 9O_2 \rightarrow 6CO_2 + 6H_2O$
q) $2C_2H_6 + 7O_2 \rightarrow 4CO_2 + 6H_2O$

Page 38 — Relative Formula Mass

Q1 a) 40 **b)** 23 **c)** 56
d) 35.5 **e)** 27 **f)** 201

Q2 a) 2 **b)** 32 **c)** 71
d) 160 **e)** 28 **f)** 38

Q3 a) 80 **b)** 36.5 **c)** 58.5
d) 28 **e)** 103 **f)** 134

Q4 a) 44 **b)** 18 **c)** 28
d) 233 **e)** 102 **f)** 461

Q5 a) 158 **b)** 154
c) 192 **d)** 74
e) 294 **f)** 331

Page 39 — Percentage Element in a Compound

Q1 a) 27.3% **k)** 82.4%
b) 42.9% **l)** 57.5%
c) 52.3% **m)** 36%
d) 54.8% **n)** 52.9%
e) 80% **o)** 51.6%
f) 50% **p)** 40%
g) 50% **q)** 38.6%
h) 40% **r)** 20.8%
i) 60% **s)** 35%
j) 11.11% **t)** 21.2%

Q2 a) M_r of CH_4 = 16 % carbon = $\frac{12}{16}$ x 100 = 75%
b) M_r of C_6H_6 = 78 % carbon = $\frac{72}{78}$ x 100 = 92.3%
c) M_r of C_2H_5OH = 46 % carbon = $\frac{24}{46}$ x 100 = 52.2%
So C_6H_6 has the greatest % mass of carbon.

Q3 a) Al_2O_3: 52.9% **b)** Na_3AlF_6: 12.9%
So Al_2O_3 has the greatest % mass of aluminium.

Q4 a) 48.3% **b)** 70%
c) 72.4% **d)** 46.7%
The iron ore with the highest % mass is: Magnetite (Fe_3O_4)

Q5 a) 39.3%
b) 28.6%
c) 100%
d) 69.6%

Page 40 — Empirical Formulae

Q1 a) $AlCl_3$
b) Sulphur trioxide — ratio of sulphur to oxygen in the compound is 1:3.
c) $Ca(OH)_2$ — calcium hydroxide
d) x = 5

Q2 a) CH_3
b) Na_3AlF_6
c) NH_3
d) $N_2H_4O_3$

Page 41 — Calculating Masses in Reactions

Q1 a) 32g **b)** 3.2g **c)** 8.8g
d) 880g **e)** 56g

Q2 a) 44g **b)** 8.8g

Q3 112 tonnes.

Q4 a) 160g **b)** 8g

Q5 a) 204kg
b) 1,889g (1.89kg)
c) 9,444g (9.44kg)
d) 1,889kg (1.89 tonnes)

Q6 a) 32g **b)** 24g

Page 42 — Simple Reversible Reactions

Q1 a) Balanced, equilibrium, equilibrium, static, downwards, upwards, activity, change, dynamic, dynamic, closed, open.
b) Dynamic
c) Closed
d) Open system. There would cease to be an equilibrium.

Q2 a) Equilibrium being established.
b) Equilibrium has been reached.
c) This is a dynamic equilibrium.

Answers — Module CD5

Q3 a) Increasing temperature will favour the product (equilibrium shifts to the right).
b) Increasing pressure will move equilibrium to left (to decrease pressure, as fewer moles of gas on left).
c) Doubling the concentration of N_2O_4 will favour the product (shift the equilibrium to the right).

Q4 a) Increasing pressure will favour product by shifting the equilibrium to the right.
b) Increasing temperature will favour reactants by shifting the equilibrium to the left.
c) Adding nitrogen will make more product.
d) Removing ammonia will also favour the forward reaction (make more ammonia).

Page 43 — Yield and Cost of Production

Q1 a) $N_{2(g)} + 3H_{2(g)} \rightleftharpoons 2NH_{3(g)}$
b) Iron catalyst
c) Catalyst speeds up the reaction.
d) Fine pellets have a large surface area and so more contact area for reactants.
e) Optimum conditions from graph are high pressure and low temperature.
f) High pressure shifts the equilibrium to the right and favours more product (4 moles of gas on left : only 2 on right).
g) Extreme high pressure is expensive and dangerous; 200 atms represents a working compromise. Lower temperatures give a higher percentage yield but take much longer to do so. 450 °C gives an acceptable yield very quickly (balance between % yield and rate of reaction).

Q2 a) i) Increasing temperature would favour backward reaction (less product).
ii) Increasing pressure would favour products (3 moles of gas on left: 2 on right).
b) Optimum conditions would be low temperature and high pressure.
c) Cost — high temperatures speeds up reaction. Less product obtained more quickly is better economically than a large yield of product obtained over a very long time.
d) Extreme pressures (1000 atm) are expensive to achieve and dangerous - need really thick reaction vessels.

Q3 90%

Q4 e, a, c, b, d – debatable.

Q5 Catalysts speed up the reaction therefore it takes less time to make the same amount of product. Catalysts also lower the operating temperature needed and this saves money.

Page 44 — Ammonia and Fertilisers

Q1 Ammonia; Haber Process; fertilisers; nitrogen; hydrogen; 450; pressure; 200; unreacted; recycled; atoms, hydrogen; atom; nitrogen.

Q2 a) Gives out heat.
b) Since the forward reaction is exothermic, increasing the temperature will stimulate the reverse reaction to try to remove this excess heat, reducing the yield of ammonia.
c) At higher temperatures the rate of reaction is greater. The lower yield is more than compensated for by the much greater reaction rate.
d) Higher pressure brings the reactants closer together so the molecules collide much more frequently and react more often. The yield is increased because the forward reaction, which tries to reduce the pressure, is favoured.

Q3 a) $4NH_{3\,(g)} + 5O_{2\,(g)} \rightarrow 4NO_{(g)} + 6H_2O_{(l)}$
nitrogen monoxide and water
b) $4NO_{(g)} + 3O_{2\,(g)} + 2H_2O_{(g)} \rightarrow 4HNO_{3\,(g)}$
c) Nitric acid.
d) Ammonia + Nitric acid → Ammonium nitrate
$NH_{3\,(g)} + HNO_{3(aq)} \rightarrow NH_4NO_{3(aq)}$
OR Ammonium hydroxide + Nitric acid → Ammonium nitrate + water
$NH_4OH_{(aq)} + HNO_{3(aq)} \rightarrow NH_4NO_{3(aq)} + H_2O_{(l)}$
e) Neutralisation.
f) Nitrogen. For making proteins and chlorophyll.

Page 45 — Ammonia and Fertilisers

Q4 a) Air
b) The reaction is reversible so the unreacted nitrogen and hydrogen are recycled to avoid wasting it.

Q5 a) Any three from: ammonium nitrate, ammonium sulphate, ammonium phosphate, urea.
b) They are soluble in water and so are easy for plants to absorb (also easily distributed by farmers).
c) Easily leached if used in excess.

Q6 a) A neutralisation reaction — ammonia acts as a base in aqueous solution and sulphuric acid is an acid.
b) ammonia + sulphuric acid → ammonium sulphate
c) $2NH_{3\,(aq)} + H_2SO_{4\,(aq)} \rightarrow (NH_4)_2SO_{4\,(aq)}$

Q7 a) Correct sequence: Excess fertilisers leach from the soil and are washed into the lake. Water plants in the lake start to grow rapidly. There is increased competition between the plants, and some die as a result. The number of microbes that feed on dead organisms increases. The microbes take more oxygen from the water for their respiration. Fish and other aquatic animals die of suffocation.
b) The plants grow more quickly because they receive additional nitrates and phosphates.
c) The plants are likely to be competing for light and space. Nitrates, phosphates and water are likely to be in excess.
d) The oxygen content of the water goes down because additional decomposers use the oxygen to respire.
e) In a eutrophic lake, the nitrates are not limited because they are being added to the community from outside. Eutrophication kills plants and eventually animals. Therefore, the microbes are not recycling the nutrient but causing increasing death followed by yet more decay.

Page 46 — Acids and Bases

Q1 a) F b) F c) T d) T e) F f) T g) T

Q2

	Name of Acid	Formula of Acid
(i)	hydrochloric	HCl
(ii)	sulphuric	H_2SO_4
(iii)	nitric	HNO_3

	Name of Alkali	Formula of Alkali
(i)	sodium hydroxide	NaOH
(ii)	ammonia solution	$NH_{3(aq)}$ / NH_4OH
(iii)	calcium hydroxide	$Ca(OH)_2$

Q3 Neutral. Water.

Q4 a) Acid.
b) Base.
c) Base.
d) Acid.
e) Acid.

Q5 a) A soluble base.
b) Something which will react with acid to give a salt and water only (e.g. a metal oxide or metal hydroxide.)
c) A chemical compound formed from the reaction between an acid and a base, metal or carbonate.

Q6 pH 1 2 3 4 5 6 7 8 9 10 11 12 13 14

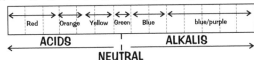

Red | Orange | Yellow | Green | Blue | blue/purple
ACIDS | NEUTRAL | ALKALIS

Q7 a) 3.
b) 7.
c) 9.
d) 11-14.
e) 14.
f) 1.

The Answers

Answers — Modules CD5 and CD6

Page 47 — Acids and Bases

Q8
1 = sulphuric acid — pH 2
2 = vinegar — pH 4
3 = water — pH 7
4 = oven cleaner — pH 12.

Q9
Sulphuric acid - sulphates, hydrochloric acid - chlorides, nitric acid - nitrates.

Q10
sulphuric acid + potassium hydroxide $\rightarrow$ water + potassium sulphate
$H_2SO_4 + 2KOH \rightarrow 2H_2O + K_2SO_4$
hydrochloric acid + calcium carbonate $\rightarrow$ water + carbon dioxide + calcium chloride
$2HCl + CaCO_3 \rightarrow H_2O + CO_2 + CaCl_2$
nitric acid + ammonia $\rightarrow$ ammonium nitrate
$HNO_3 + NH_3 \rightarrow NH_4NO_3$

Q11
Water.

Q12
H^+ from acid and OH^- from alkali.

Q13
Base.

Q14
a) Lemon juice on wasp stings.
b) Bicarbonate of soda for bee stings.
c) Dock leaves for nettle stings.
b) and c) might be reversed.

CD6 — The Periodic Table

Page 48 — Atoms

Q1 a) Smallest particle of an element with the properties of that element. The basic building block of all matter.
b) 3.
c) Protons, neutrons and electrons.
d) Small structure consisting of protons and neutrons at the centre of the atom making up almost all the mass.
e) A group of electrons with the same energy.

Q2
A: Nucleus　　　B: Electron　　　C: Shell

Q3

Particle	Mass	Charge	Where it is found
Proton	1	+1	In the nucleus
Electron	Negligible	-1	Orbiting the nucleus
Neutron	1	0	In the nucleus

Q4 a) In the nucleus.　**b)** Empty space.

Q5 The electrons.

Q6 7

Q7 a) The number of protons.
b) The total number of protons and neutrons.
c) A = Mass number; Z = Atomic number;
A–Z = number of neutrons.
d) 3
e) 3
f) 4
g) Atomic number (Z) indicates the number of protons (which defines an element).

Q8 a) protons: 6,　electrons: 6, neutrons: 6.
b) protons: 19,　electrons: 19,　neutrons: 20.
c) protons: 1,　electrons: 1, neutrons: 0.

Q9 a) Isotopes are different atomic forms of the same element; they have the same number of protons but a different number of neutrons.
Carbon 14 (^{14}C).
b) No, because their electron structure is identical.

Page 49 — The Periodic Table

Q1 a) A vertical column.
b) A horizontal row.
c) Approximately 100.
d) Order of atomic number / proton number.
e) Same number of electrons in outer shell hence similar chemical properties, form similarly charged ions, etc.
f) The number of shells of electrons that they have.
g) 1.
h) Group 7.

Q2 a) H, I;　**h)** F;
b) C;　**i)** A, E;
c) B;　**j)** H, I, D;
d) B;　**k)** G;
e) D;　**l)** A;
f) A;　**m)** H, I.
g) C, D, G, H, I;

Q3 An extra full shell of electrons.

Page 50 — The Periodic Table

Q4 a) i) Left hand side.
ii) Right hand side.
b) Between Groups 2 and 3.
c) Francium.

Q5 Atomic number, protons, relative atomic mass, argon, potassium.

Q6 They all have two electrons in their outer shells (they're also all metals).

Q7 It tells us that an atom of sodium has 11 electrons, 11 protons and 12 neutrons (and from this electronic configurations can be worked for the atom).

Q8 a)

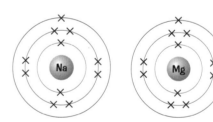

Magnesium has two electrons to lose, sodium has one.
b) Magnesium is in Period 3 — it has three non-empty electron shells.
c) Magnesium has two electrons in its outer shell which both have to be removed to form the Mg ion — the sodium ion is formed by the removal of only one electron. This requires less energy, therefore sodium is more reactive.

Page 51 — Electron Shells

Q1 a) The negative charge of the electrons keeps them attracted to the positively charged nucleus.
b) Shell

Q2

Electron shell	Maximum number of electrons in the shell
1st	2
2nd	8
3rd	8

Answers — Module CD6

Q3

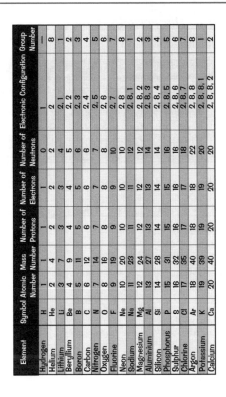

Q4 a) The number of outer electrons determines the group that the element is in.
 b) All Noble gases have a full outer shell / Every element whose atoms have a full outer shell is a Noble gas.
 c) 7
 d) 8
 e) Chemical properties.

Q5 a) It's in Group 2.
 b) Metal
 c) Any Group 2 element, eg. magnesium, calcium etc.

Page 52 — Electron Shells

Q1

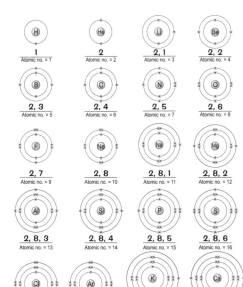

Page 53 — Ions

Q1

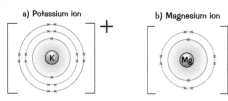

Q2

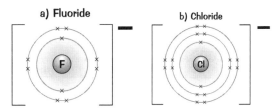

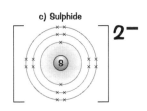

Q3 a) Positive.
 b) Negative.

Q4 a) As they have lost an electron and thus have one more proton than electrons (only needed to lose one electron to have a full outer shell).
 b) As they have gained an electron and thus have one more electron than protons (only needed to gain one electron to have a full outer shell).
 c) 2 +
 d) 2 −
 e) To form a C^{++} ion would take a massive amount of energy as four electrons are removed, so carbon normally bonds covalently.

Q5 a) Sodium chloride formed.

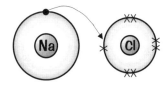

 b)

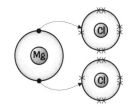

The Answers

Answers — Module CD6

Q6

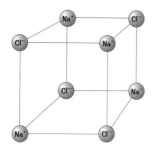

Q7 a) Sodium
b) Oxide
c) Sulphide
d) Nitrate
e) Sulphate
f) Iodide
g) Fluoride
h) Potassium
i) Calcium
j) Magnesium
k) Phosphate
l) Hydrogen

Q8 MgO, NaF, Na_2O, $MgSO_4$, Na_2SO_4.

Q9 Because when they are solid there are no free moving ions (they are all involved in bonding), but they are free to move in liquid form or in solution.

Q10 a, b.

Page 54 — Symbols, Formulae and Equations

Q1 Fe, Pb, Zn, Sn, Cu.

Q2

Name	Formula	Number of atoms of each element present in one particle
Zinc oxide	ZnO	1 zinc 1 oxygen
Magnesium oxide	MgO	1 magnesium 1 oxygen
Sodium chloride	NaCl	1 sodium 1 chlorine
Carbon dioxide	CO_2	1 carbon 2 oxygen
Sodium hydroxide	NaOH	1 sodium 1 oxygen 1 hydrogen
Potassium hydroxide	KOH	1 potassium 1 oxygen 1 hydrogen
Magnesium chloride	$MgCl_2$	1 magnesium 2 chlorine
Hydrogen	H_2	2 hydrogen
Chlorine	Cl_2	2 Chlorine

Q3 Chloride, Oxide, Sulphide.

Q4 a) Brine.
b) Ionic compounds such as sodium chloride do not conduct in solid form and their melting points are very high.

Q5 Industrial, rock salt, brine, electrolysis, Na^+, Cl^-, chloride, lose, chlorine, chlorine atoms, chlorine molecule, H^+, gain, hydrogen, hydrogen atoms, hydrogen molecule, sodium hydroxide.

Page 55 — Group 8: The Noble Gases

Q1 a) Non-reactive.
b) They have a full outer shell of electrons, making them stable so they have no need to react.
c) In order: Noble, 8, Periodic, full, shell, electrons, inert, low, increase, radon, helium, individual, diatomic, 1%.

Q2 a) Increase down the group.
b)

Noble Gas	Atomic Number	Density g/cm³	Melting Point °C	Boiling Point °C
Helium	2	0.00017	-272	-269
Neon	10	0.00084	-248	-246
Argon	18	0.0016	-189	-186
Krypton	36	0.0034	-157	-153
Xenon	54	0.006	-112	-107
Radon	86	0.01	-71	-62

c) Increase in atomic mass

Q3 It gives out a bright light when a current is passed through it.

Q4 Light bulbs. Gives an inert atmosphere and stops burning of the filament.

Q5 Argon is denser than air, helium is less dense so the balloon rises rather than falls.

Q6 a)

Noble Gas	Symbol	Atomic Number	Mass Number	No. of Protons	No. of Electrons	No. of Neutrons
Helium	He	2	4	2	2	2
Neon	Ne	10	20	10	10	10
Argon	Ar	18	40	18	18	22
Krypton	Kr	36	84	36	36	48
Xenon	Xe	54	131	54	54	77
Radon	Rn	86	222	86	86	136

b) **i)** neon   **ii)** helium, neon   **iii)** argon, neon, helium.

Page 56 — Group 1: The Alkali Metals

Q1 a) Symbols: Li, Na, K, Rb.
b) As you go down the Group the atoms have more shells to accommodate more electrons.
c) Rubidium.
d) i) Rb between 39 and 688°C.
ii) K between 63 and 759°C.

Q2 Cs, Rb, K, Na, Li. Reactivity increases down the Group because the outermost electron moves further away from the nucleus, so is lost more easily.

Q3 A → 3, B → 1, C → 2.

Q4 F, T, F, T, T

Q5 a)

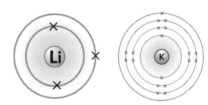

b) Lose an electron.
c) 1+
d) Li^+, K^+
e) Potassium — It is easier for the outer electron of potassium to be lost as potassium atoms are bigger and the outer electron is further away from the nucleus, so is less firmly held. The alkali metals lose this electron in reactions.

Page 57 — Reactions of the Alkali Metals

Q1 They form an alkaline solution in water.

Q2 They are stored under oil as they react with the oxygen in air to form oxides.

Q3 a) They're all alkaline, so the pH would be greater than 7.
b) Hydrogen. Put a lighted splint into the test tube — if it's hydrogen it'll give a squeaky pop.

Q4 a) Lithium + oxygen → lithium oxide ($4Li + O_2 \rightarrow 2Li_2O$)
b) $Li_2O + H_2SO_4 \rightarrow H_2O + Li_2SO_4$

Q5 a) $2Na + Cl_2 \rightarrow 2NaCl$
b) $4Li + O_2 \rightarrow 2Li_2O$
c) $2Li + 2H_2O \rightarrow 2LiOH + H_2$

Q6 a) They react violently igniting the H_2 produced.
b) Oxide layer forms very quickly.
c) The outer electron is quite far from the nucleus of the atom, and is less firmly held, so very easily lost.

Q7 a) Sodium hydroxide + hydrogen,
Lithium hydroxide + hydrogen.
b) i) $2K_{(s)} + 2H_2O_{(l)} \rightarrow 2KOH_{(aq)} + H_{2\,(g)}$
ii) s: solid; l: liquid; aq: aqueous; g: gas.

Answers — Modules CD6 and PD4

Page 58 — Group VII: The Halogens

Q1 They all have 7 electrons in the outer shell.

Q2 a) Molecules contain two atoms each – Cl_2, Br_2, etc.
b) **i)** Cl_2 **ii)** I_2 .

Q3 a) Ionic.
b) 1–
c) A salt, eg. sodium chloride, potassium chloride etc.

Q4 It becomes increasingly harder for the halogens to gain an electron (due to increased electron shielding by inner shells), whereas it becomes increasingly easier for the alkali metals to lose an electron, as you go down the groups.

Q5 $2K_{(s)} + Cl_{2(g)} \rightarrow 2KCl_{(s)}$

Q6 a) Lithium + chlorine $\rightarrow$ lithium chloride
Sodium + chlorine $\rightarrow$ sodium chloride
Potassium + chlorine $\rightarrow$ potassium chloride
b) Lithium + bromine $\rightarrow$ lithium bromide
Sodium + bromine $\rightarrow$ sodium bromide
Potassium + bromine $\rightarrow$ potassium bromide
c) Lithium + fluorine $\rightarrow$ lithium fluoride
Sodium + fluorine $\rightarrow$ sodium fluoride
Potassium + fluorine $\rightarrow$ potassium fluoride

Q7 a) Bromine (orange/brown) forming in the tube.
b) Chlorine.
c) Chlorine is more reactive than bromine, so displaces the bromine from the sodium bromide.
d) **i)** Fluorine + sodium iodide $\rightarrow$ sodium fluoride + iodine.
ii) Chlorine + sodium bromide $\rightarrow$ sodium chloride + bromine.
iii) Bromine + potassium iodide $\rightarrow$ potassium bromide + iodine.

Q8 Fluorine: used in toothpastes and water to reduce dental decay;
Chlorine: sterilising swimming pools and tap water, pesticides;
Iodine: sterilising wounds.

Page 59 — Transition Metals

Q1 Between Group 2 and Group 3.

Q2 a) Group two elements only form 2+ ions.
b) **i)** XO
ii) X_2O_3

Q3 $1 \rightarrow B$, $2 \rightarrow C$, $3 \rightarrow A$.

Q4 a) **i)** Fencing/gates, manhole covers etc.
ii) Galvanising iron.
iii) Wiring/pipes.
b) Others will be corroded by the water.

Q5

Conductivity		Density	Malleability	Melting point
Heat	Electricity			
Good	Good	High	High	High

b) **i)** YCl. **ii)** Y_2O. **iii)** YO.

Q6 A chemical that speeds up a reaction without itself being changed or used up.

Q7 a) Thermal decomposition.
b) Zinc carbonate $\rightarrow$ zinc oxide + carbon dioxide
c) $CuCO_3 \rightarrow CuO + CO_2$

Q8 a) A precipitate is formed if there are transition metal ions present.
b) The forming of a green / grey precipitate.

PD4 — Using Electricity

Page 60 — Current, Voltage and Resistance

Q1 Complete, charged, circuit, electrons, metal, positive.

Q2

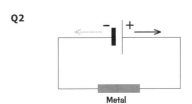

Metal

Q3 Current; positive; negative; opposite direction to.

Q4

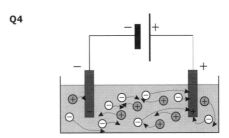

Q5 Liquids, charged particles (ions), dissolved, sodium chloride solution, sodium chloride, negative, positive.

Q6 Metals consist of positively charged ions which are surrounded by a sea of electrons. These electrons are free to move which lets an electrical current pass through the material.

Page 61 — Circuit Symbols and Devices

Q7

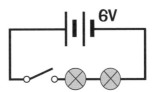

Q8

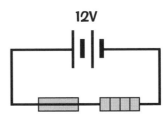

Q9 From top: 38.3A; 10A; 2Ω; 0.1A; 3Ω ; 7.5V.

Q10 23Ω.

Q11 0.5A.

Q12 a)

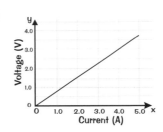

Answers — Module PD4

b) 0.75Ω.
c) Resistor.
d) Voltage proportional to current (straight line graph through origin).

Q13 **a)** 1V. **b)** 3V. **c)** 1.5A. **d)** 0.6A. **e)** 1.5Ω. **f)** 3Ω.

Q14 Different wires have different **resistances**, hence the different **slopes** on a graph. As the **temperature** of the filament **increases**, the resistance increases. The graph with the steeper slope is a **thick** wire of the same material as it has a **lower** resistance. Current in a diode can only be in **one direction**.

Page 62 — Circuit Symbols and Devices

Q1

CIRCUIT SYMBOL	NAME FOR CIRCUIT SYMBOL	WHAT IT DOES
	Cell	Provides potential difference/voltage.
	LDR	Resistance changes with light intensity.
	Loudspeaker	Converts electrical energy into sound energy.
	Voltmeter	Measures voltage across a circuit.
	Fuse	Wire inside breaks if current is too high, protecting the appliance.
	Fixed resistor	To determine the current in a circuit.
	Thermistor	Resistance changes with temperature.
	Open Switch	Stops current flowing.
	Diode	Lets current flow in one direction only.
	Variable resistor	Adjusted to alter the current in a circuit.
	Motor	Produces motion from electrical energy.
	Ammeter	Measures the current in a circuit.

Q2 **a)** Rate of flow of charged particles. **b)** Reduces current. **c)** Allows current in one direction only. **d)** Unit of power. **e)** Liquid containing ions. **f)** Unit of current. **g)** Measures current. **h)** Measures voltage. **i)** Metal of low resistance. **j)** Unit of voltage.

Q3

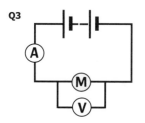

Page 63 — Circuit Symbols and Devices

Q4

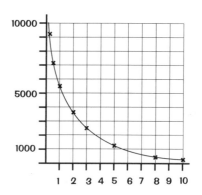

a) It decreases.
b) It increases.
c) With increasing light intensity, the slope of the curve becomes less steep → resistance decreases more slowly.
d) Automatic night light; LDR increases resistance in the dark, the circuit 'detects' the increase and turns the light on. Burglar detector; could detect a torch in a similar way.

Q5 a) Resistance increases as temperature decreases.
b) 110Ω.
c) Car engine temperature sensors, electronic thermostats.
d) 30°C to 20°C, so temperature change is 10°C.

Q6 a) DC.
b) AC.
c) DC flows in the same direction all of the time. AC keeps switching direction.
d) The CRO on the left is AC, the one on the right DC.

Page 64 — Energy Change

Q1 a) Current, I, **Amp(ere)s**, **A**; **Resistance**, **R**, ohms, Ω. **Energy**, E, joules, **J**; Electrical Charge, Q, **coulombs**, **C**; **Time**, t, seconds, **s**; Power, **P**, watts, **W**.
b) 4 coulombs, 12 coulombs. 3 seconds, 6A, 60 coulombs.

Q2 a) 9000J.
b) 3000J.
c) 9J.

Q3 a) It's converted to heat energy.
b) More heat energy is produced.
c) More heat energy is produced, because a higher voltage means a higher current.

Q4 a) is one joule per coulomb
b) is charge × voltage
c) is one coulomb every second
d) is the energy transferred per unit of charge passed
e) is current × time.

Q5 a) i) 0.26A
ii) 11.96A
iii) 3.48A
iv) 6.52A
b) 46W

Answers — Modules PD4 and PD5

Page 65 — Energy Change

Q6 a)

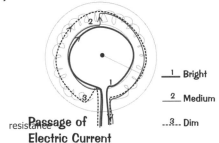

Inside a dimmer switch

resistance — Passage of Electric Current

1 — Bright
2 — Medium
3 — Dim

b)

Brightness of Lights	Current(A)	Resistance(Ω)
Dim	1.0	6.0
Medium brightness	2.0	3.0
Bright	3.0	2.0

c) Resistance increased $\rightarrow$ current falls.
d) Resistance decreased $\rightarrow$ current rises.

Q7 10V, 45J, 20C, 500C, 900J.   light intensity

Q8 a) Energy input in given time will be x2. Temp rise will be x2.
b) Energy input in given time will be x2. Temp rise will be x2.
c) No change.

Q9 a) B
b) C
c) D

Page 66 — Static Electricity

Q1 a) are attracted to each other.
b) is caused by friction.
c) move, never the positive charges.
d) builds up if charge builds up.
e) is lost if a charged rod is moved away.
f) the greater the voltage.
g) by connecting it to Earth.
h) repel each other.
i) if electrons are rubbed on.
j) repel each other.
k) if electrons are rubbed off.

Q2 a) & b)

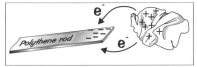

Polythene rod

c) They move, due to induced charges in the paper or cork.

Q3 Increases, voltage, high, earthed, spark.

Q4 a) Air rushing past gives the car a +ve charge. When you get out and touch the door electrons flow from earth, through you, to neutralise the +ve charge on the car.

b) As you walk on carpet, you can pick up or gain electrons which creates a static charge. When you touch the pipe, you earth the charge and may feel a slight shock.

Q5 Static charges on the jumper give rise to sparks and shocks when the jumper is removed, due to the movement of electrons as the charges redistribute themselves.

Q6 a) Near grain shoot (also spelled chute), paper rollers, fuel tanks
b) Depends on which hazard is chosen.
c) Make the nozzles or rollers out of metal so the charge is conducted away instead of building up. Put earthing straps between the fuel tank and the fuel pipe.

Q7

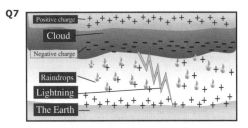

Positive charge
Cloud
Negative charge
Raindrops
Lightning
The Earth

Page 67 — Static Electricity — Examples

Q1 Spray painting, photocopiers, inkjet printers, dust removal.

Q2 Nozzle, fine (or thin), electrostatically (or electrically) charged, voltage, metal, positively, negatively (these two could be the other way around), attracted, opposite, repelled, same, deflection,voltage, varied (altered or changed), deflected, small (or tiny).

Q3 F, C, H, B, J, D, A, I, E, G

Module PD5 — Applications of Physics

Page 68 — Electric Motors

Q1

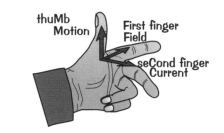

thuMb Motion
First finger Field
seCond finger Current

Q2 a) Anticlockwise.
b) From N to S.
c) Upwards.
d) Reverse current or field.
e) Stronger magnets, increase the current.
f) No force. Current must be at an angle between 0 and 90° to the magnetic field to experience a force.

Q3 Bar moves to the left with a DC current. With AC of a reasonably high frequency and a bar of fair mass there should be little movement as the bar is pulled in opposite directions during the different parts of the cycle, but the bar will vibrate at the frequency of the supply.

Q4 coil, up, right, down, turn, torque, current, forces.

Q5 a) split ring commutator
b) carbon brushes
c) electric motor
d) coil (armature)
e) polarity

Page 69 — Electromagnetic Induction

Q1 a) Movement of the magnet in the coil induces a voltage. This leads to a current in the circuit making the buzzer sound.
b) No. No movement, so no induced voltage.
c) Move the magnet faster by making the train go faster; use a stronger magnet.

Answers — Module PD5

Q2 a) Needle stays at zero; Needle moves to the left; Needle moves further to the left.
b) N on left, S on right. (The induced pole acts to stop (or slow down) the movement of the magnet.)
c) Pull the magnet out or put the magnet in the other way round.

Q3 a) i) Increased current.
ii) Increased current.
iii) No current — lines of magnetic field not cut through.
b) Dynamo effect.

Q4 Simple generator: c, d, e.
Power station generator: b, e, g.
Dynamo: a, c, e, h.

Page 70 — Electromagnetic Induction

Q5 The strength of the magnet. The area of the coil. The number of turns on the coil. The speed of the movement.

Q6 Rotate, magnetic, motor, slip, swap, voltage, faster, more, higher, voltage.

Q7

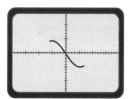

a) Greatest, horizontal, cuts, rapidly.
b) Zero, vertical, field.

Q8 **a** and **d** are step-up. **b** and **c** are step-down.

Q9 460V, 115V, 6V, 72V.

Q10 a) A region where magnetic materials and wires carrying currents experience a force acting on them. In the case of transformers, these fields change with time so a voltage is induced in the secondary coil.
b) Where input voltage is fed in.
c) The process by which the AC voltage in the primary coil produces an AC voltage in the secondary coil.
d) Where output voltage is produced.
e) For a transformer it means the number of turns on the primary coil divided by the number of turns on the secondary coil, written as a ratio (using whole numbers).

Q11 Transformers work by induction. Induction only occurs when the current (and hence the magnetic field) is changing (alternating).

Page 71 — The National Grid

Q1 a) Power=$I^2 \times R$.
b) Power loss is 4 times as great.
c) To transmit the same power you can either use high current/low voltage or low current/high voltage.
But the greater the current, the greater the power loss — so a high voltage is used.
d) 52174.
e) 4182.

Q2 a) They are loose so the contacts do not swap every half turn. That means that generators produce AC voltage.
b) As the coil moves between the poles of the magnet it 'cuts' through lines of magnetic flux. This induces voltage and current across the coil which is transferred from the coil by the slip rings.
c) i) Decreases.
ii) Increased.
iii) Increases, increased **or** decreases, decreased.

Page 72 — The National Grid

Q3 a) (from left to right) Boiler, Turbine, Generator, Transformer, Grid/pylon.
b) Coal, oil, gas (any order), uranium fuel, steam, turbine, generator, induction, magnetic.

Q4 a) to keep the current low.
b) is best calculated using $V \times I$.
c) you need a high voltage or a high current.
d) due to resistance of the cables.
e) equals $I^2 \times R$.
f) to keep the current low.
g) requires transformers as well as big pylons with huge insulators.
h) for efficient transmission.
i) to bring it back to safe useable levels.
j) because transformers don't work with DC.

Q5 a) Voltage, current, power, resistance.
b) ohms, amps, watts, volts.

Q6 V & V; I & A; P & W; R & Ω.

Q7 a) send from one place to another.
b) alternating current.
c) direct current.
d) motor driven by steam.
e) place for generating and distributing electrical power.
f) changes the voltage of an alternating current.

Page 73 — Work Done and Power

Q1 a) Work done = Force × Distance
b)

Work Done
6.72J
4.48J
5.76J
8.26J
4.05J

Joules (J).
c) Friction and air resistance.
d) 567 J, 38W.

Q2 a) 1 050 000 J = 1050 kJ = 1.05 MJ
b) 1170 kJ (= (900 × 700) + (600 × 900))
c) 955 kJ (= (1200 × 700) + (100 × 1150))
Yes, I would save energy, provided that I could push the car up the hill.

Q3 a) Scott - 190 kJ; Sheila - 170 kJ.
b) The motor would not be 100% efficient, and the motor will also be doing work pushing the boat and driver along.
c) 219.4 kJ (= 4 × (30 × 720) + (280 × 475))
d) 110s.

Page 74 — Kinetic Energy and Potential Energy

Q1 a) K.E. = $\frac{1}{2}mv^2$
b) m = mass of object, v = velocity of object.
c) All moving objects have kinetic energy.

Q2 a) P.E. = mgh
b) m = mass of object,
g = acceleration due to gravity,
h = height gained or lost.
c) An object gains or loses gravitational potential energy when its height (ie. altitude) changes.

Q3 a) True
b) False
c) False
d) False
e) True
f) False
g) False
h) False (but true if they both have the same mass)

Answers — Module PD5

Q4

Time (s)	Velocity (m/s)	Kinetic Energy (J)
0.0	0	0
0.5	10	131,500
1.0	30	1,183,500
1.5	45	2,662,875

Q5   **a)** 320 J, **b)** 875 J (greatest), **c)** 750 J, **d)** 180 J, **e)** 156 J.

Q6 a)   4.5 MJ
b)   2.7 MJ
c)   1.275 MJ

Page 75 — Kinetic Energy and Potential Energy

Q7 a)   772 kJ (= ½ × 2920 × 23²)
b)   35 MJ (= 2920 × 10 × 1200)
c)   12 kJ (= 20 × 10 × 60)
d)   35 m/s
e)   Energy is lost due to air resistance and any collisions with the mountain side — sound and heat is generated.

Q8

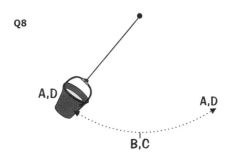

A,D   A,D   B,C

Q9 a)   9 J (= 0.3 × 10 × 3)
b)   7.75 m/s (P.E. = K.E. = 9 J)
c)   7.4 J (= ½ × 0.3 × 7²)
d)   2.5 m (K.E. = P.E. = 7.4 J)
e)   The energy is changed to heat and sound energy as it hits the ground.
f)   82%.

Q10

Name	Weight (N)	Time (s)	Potential Energy Gained (J)	Power (W)
Alex	520	14	6240	446
Billie	450	16	5400	338
Jack	600	15	7200	480

Page 76 — Digital and Analogue Signals

Q1 a)   Digital and analogue.
b)   The amplitude and frequency of analogue signals vary continuously. Digital signals take one of only two values.
c)   Analogue: watch, dimmer switch, speedometer.
Digital: watch, computer, on/off switch.

Q2 a)   FALSE - analogue varies continuously, not digital.
b)   TRUE.
c)   TRUE.
d)   TRUE.
e)   FALSE - analogue signals lose quality, not digital.
f)   TRUE.

Q3 a)   Because as signals travel, they become weaker.
b)   They pick up noise (random additions).
c)   Digital signals retain their original form exactly; analogue ones are altered by amplification.

Q6

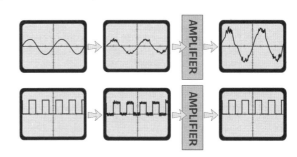

Q7 a)   DAC — digital to analogue converter.
ADC — analogue to digital converter.
b)   A modem

Page 77 — EM Waves for Communication

Q1 a)   same speed
b)   Radio, microwaves, infra-red, light (any order).
c)   Reflected, refracted, diffracted (any order).

Q2 a)   Critical angle;
b)   Total internal reflection; optical.
c)   i) Boosted/amplified;
ii) Data/information;
iii) Reflection; boosting/amplifying
d)   endoscope.

Q3 a)   True
b)   False — replace microwaves with infra red.
c)   True
d)   False — replace only visible light with all EM waves.
e)   True
f)   True — debatable as X-rays are *relatively* safe compared with the high risks of investigative surgery including death under anaesthetic, post-operative shock and infection, but are still highly hazardous. Ultrasound might be suggested as an alternative to X-rays for medical imaging but the two techniques give very different results which is why X-rays are still widely used.
g)   False — replace infra red with ultraviolet.
h)   True
i)   True
j)   True

Page 78 — EM Waves for Communication

Q4 a)

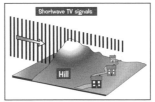

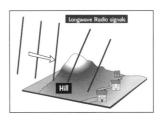

b)   Mountains diffract long-wave radio waves more effectively than TV signals, leading to a better reception of radio than TV signals.

Answers — Modules PD5 and PD6

Q5   Clockwise from top:
satellite receiver and transmitter
ground based receiver
ground based transmitter

upwards, ground based transmitter, satellite receiver dish,
transmits, direction, ground, world.

Q6   The ionosphere.

Q7 a)   Between and within different layers of the atmosphere.
   b)   They travel at different speeds in the different parts of the
atmosphere.
   c)   At the edge of transmission dishes.

PD6 — Earth, space and Nuclear Radiation

Page 79 — Basic Mechanics

Q1 a)   Pegasus: $(12,000 - 0) \div 8 = 1500$ m/s^2
Icarus: $(6000 - 0) \div 16 = 375$ m/s^2
   b) $F = m \times a = 380,000 \times 375 = 142,500,000$ N
   c)   Gravitational force $= m \times g = 500,000 \times 10 = 5,000,000$ N
Another name for the gravitational force is the weight.
   d)   Its direction of motion.
   e)   The forces must all be balanced.
   f)   It accelerates towards the centre of the Earth.

Q2 a)   Its velocity is not constant because the satellite's direction of
motion is constantly changing.
   b)   The satellite must be accelerating since it has a constantly
changing velocity.
   c)   The centripetal force.
   d)   The force of gravity.

Q3   The fact that the shuttle moves can be explained by the law,
"When an object exerts a force on a second object, the second
object exerts an equal but opposite force on the first object".
In this case, the shuttle exerts a force on the burning exhaust
gases coming out of it. The law tells us that the burning
exhaust gases exert an equal force in the opposite direction on
the shuttle. This force pushes the shuttle forward, causing it to
accelerate.

Page 80 — Basic Mechanics

Q4 a)   False - they will land at the same time, since the only force
acting is gravity. There is no air on the Moon to provide air
resistance.
   b)   False - F = ma.
   c)   True.
   d)   True.
   e)   False.

Q5   The downward force acting on all **falling** objects is gravity,
which would make them fall at the **same** rate if it wasn't for
air **resistance**. The terminal velocity of any object is
determined by its **drag** in comparison to the **weight** of it.

Q6 a)   60.0 m/s
   b)   (i) 19.5 m/s (ii) 45.0 m/s
   c)   18 s
   d)   The additional drag of the parachute gives rise to a resultant
upward force that decelerates her. As she slows down,
the upward drag force decreases until it balances her
weight, at which point she reaches a terminal velocity.
   e)   Yes. Speed decreases until drag equals weight.

Q7 a)   50 N ; left.
   b)   0.5 N ; up.
   c)   15 N ; up.
   d)   0.05 N ; down.

Page 81 — The Planets

Q1 a)   False – the sun generates energy by nuclear
fusion, mainly of hydrogen into helium.
   b)   False – planets are observed because of the light
that they reflect from the Sun.
   c)   True – the smaller Moon orbits the larger Earth.
   d)   True – all the planets in the solar system orbit
around the Sun, a very massive object.
   e)   True – the force of gravity attracts comets,
planets, and satellites and determines their
orbits around larger bodies.
   f)   False – all planets follow elliptical orbits
with the Sun at one focus of the ellipse.
   g)   False – the main reason for other stars looking
so dim in comparison to the Sun is because
they are much further away from us.

Q2   The diagram should look like this:

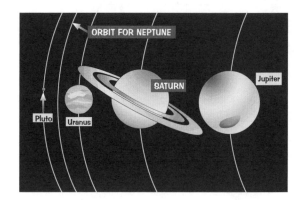

Page 82 — The Universe and its Origin

Q1   From smallest to largest: meteorite,
comet (nucleus), planet, star, galaxy.

Q2   Big Bang theory. This theory says that the Universe
started with a huge explosion of energy and matter.

Q3   Most astronomers now believe that the Universe began
with a huge explosion which we call the **Big Bang**. This
theory is supported by strong scientific **evidence**. About
35 years ago astronomers detected microwave
background radiation coming from all directions in
space. This radiation is thought to have been released in
the Big Bang. Also, by examining the **red shift** of the
spectrum of stars, astronomers have discovered that the
Universe is
expanding. The expansion of the Universe suggests that
some sort of initial **explosion** took place. This is further
evidence in support of the Big Bang **theory**.

Q4 a)   The Doppler effect.
   b)   The frequency increases.
   c)   The frequency decreases.
   d)   A car sounds its horn as it passes you — the horn sounds
higher as the car drives towards you and lower when it drives
away from you. The pitch of the engine noise also seems to
fall as it drives past.
Driving past a shop whose alarm is sounding — the pitch of
the note will seem to drop. The pitch of an ambulance
siren will sound higher as it approaches you, and lower
when going away from you.

Answers — Module PD6

Q5 a) The wave looks like this:

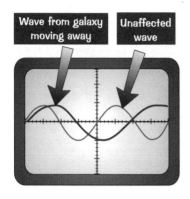

b) The sound falls in pitch.
c) Electromagnetic radiation with a very small wavelength and high frequency (gamma radiation).

Q6 a) True **b)** True **c)** True
d) False **e)** True **f)** False
g) True **h)** True

Page 83 — The Life Cycle of Stars

Q1 a) A heavyweight star more massive than our Sun (observations suggest masses greater than approximately 4×Solar mass).
b) Because they are very hot and give off a lot of light.
c) These stages don't give off their own visible light, only IR radiation. Also, the protostars are hidden by quite thick gas and dust clouds.
d) Gravity.
e) Main sequence (C).
f) E, Supernova.
g) The surface of the star gets cooler.
h) It is much denser (tons per cm³).
i) The life-span of a typical star is billions of years. Unfortunately, astronomers haven't been around for that long and are unlikely to be so in the future! So they examine many different stars of different ages to get the big picture.
j) Nuclear fusion.

Q2 a) A. White Dwarf
b) B. Supernova
c) C. Planetary nebula. This could form a new solar system in the future.

Page 84 — The Future of the Universe

Q1 a) How fast the galaxies are moving apart; the total mass in the Universe.
b) The speed is easy to measure, the total mass is more difficult.

Q2 Visible — Supergiant stars, white dwarf stars, main sequence stars
Invisible — Interstellar dust, black holes, black dwarves, dust between the galaxies

Q3 a) Gravity.
b) The Universe would carry on expanding forever.

Q4 a) The rate of expansion is getting smaller.
b) The graphs look like this:

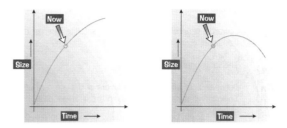

Q5 The first calculations made by scientists about the age of the **Universe** gave an age of only **2 billion years**. This was a big surprise because previous **radioactivity** measurements on rocks from the **Earth** (and later the **Moon**) showed the age of the Solar system to be about **4.5 billion years**. The **Solar System** can't be older than the **Universe**.

Q6 a) The Big Crunch is one possible future for the Universe. It is what happens if the Universe stops expanding, and collapses in on itself. It's the Big Bang in reverse.
b) At least 15 billion years (the age of the Universe). It will take as long to collapse as it has had to expand.

Q7 The graph should look like this:

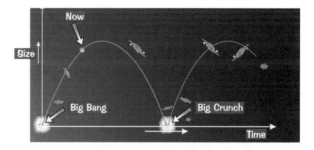

Page 85 — Searching for Life on Other Planets

Q1 It's essential that there's **water** in **liquid** form.
The **temperature** must be just right — not too **hot** and not too **cold**.
Life can't exist in extreme atmospheric **pressures**.
A suitable atmosphere is required. It protects life from harmful **UV radiation**.

Q2 a) **S**earch for **E**xtra **T**errestrial **I**ntelligence. SETI looks for radio signals coming to Earth from other planets.
b) If the signal was made from a narrow band of wavelengths.

Q3 a) Scientists are searching for life on other planets and moons in our **solar system** by sending **spacecraft** to them. There have been some **missions** to Mars, for example, which have involved both orbiting and landing craft, both looking for any tell-tale signs of **life**. Studying **meteorites**, rocks which have fallen to Earth from space, is another way in which scientists are searching for signs of **extraterrestrial** life. Quite recently, scientists analysed a meteorite from **Mars** using high-powered **microscopes**. They found what could possibly be small **fossils** of ancient Martian **bacteria**. Astronomers are also using **telescopes** to search for other **stars** with planets orbiting them. There is now strong **evidence** to suggest that such planets have been found.

Answers — Module PD6

Page 86 — The Three Types of Radiation

Q1 a) γ
b) α
c) α
d) all three
e) β
f) β
g) γ
h) α
i) β
j) α
k) all three

Q2 Alpha: Smoke detectors
Beta: Testing paper thickness, medical tracers.
Gamma: Treating cancer, sterilising equipment, medical tracers.

Q3 Throughout our daily lives we are all **exposed** to nuclear radiation from **natural** sources. This is commonly called **background** radiation. Some of this radiation comes from the **rocks** and **soil** around us. This is because they both contain small amounts of **radioactive** substances. Another source of background radiation comes from **outer space**. All around us, radiation called **cosmic rays** bombards the Earth and adds to the natural radiation levels.

Page 87 — Radioactivity and Half-Life

Q1 a) Ionisation is the process of removing electrons from or adding electrons to an atom. The atom becomes a charged particle (ion).
b) It becomes ionised. An electron is knocked off the argon atom, leaving a positive argon ion and a free electron.
c) The electrons move to the top (+ve) plate and the argon ions move to the (–ve) plate. Electrons travel around the circuit to combine with these argon ions. (Neutral argon atoms are formed at the –ve plate).
d) There can be no ionisation in a vacuum (no atoms to ionise), so there are no moving charges, and therefore no current.

Q2 The **radioactivity** of a sample always **decreases** over time. Each time a decay happens, **alpha**, **beta** or **gamma** radiation is emitted. This means a radioactive **nucleus** has decayed. The problem with trying to measure the time for all the atoms to decay is that the activity never reaches **zero**. The half-life is the **time** taken for **half** of the radioactive **atoms** now present to **decay**.

Q3 a)

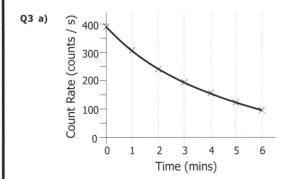

b) 3 minutes.

Q4 a) 15 minutes.
b) 45 minutes.
c) About 31 counts per second.
d) 3 hours.

Page 88 — Radioactivity and Half-Life

Q1 a)

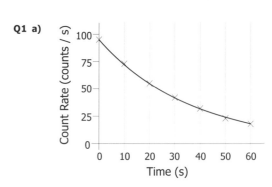

b) 23 ±1 secs.
c) Possible methods: Measure the activity over a long time period; measure a large sample; shield sample and measuring apparatus.

Q2 a) 4.5 billion years.
b) 0 years.

Q3 a) $^{210}_{82}Pb \rightarrow ^{210}_{83}Bi + ^{0}_{-1} \rightarrow ^{210}_{84}Po + 2^{0}_{-1}$
b) 5 days (to nearest day).
c) $^{206}_{82}Pb$ (Mass Number = 206).

Q4 a) 25s.
b) The count rate is very low. A time of at least a few minutes is needed to record a significant number of counts.